A Holistic Vet's

PRESCRIPTION

for a Healthy Herd

A Guide to Livestock Nutrition, Free-Choice
Minerals, and Holistic Cattle Care

A Holistic Vet's
PRESCRIPTION
for a Healthy Herd

A Guide to Livestock Nutrition, Free-Choice Minerals, and Holistic Cattle Care

Richard J. Holliday, DVM, and Jim Helfter

Acres U.S.A.
Austin, Texas

A Holistic Vet's Prescription
for a Healthy Herd

Acres U.S.A.
P.O. Box 301209
Austin, Texas 78703 U.S.A.
512-892-4400 • fax 512-892-4448
info@acresusa.com • *www.acresusa.com*

Printed in the United States of America

Front cover photography © gemenacom/iStock/Thinkstock
Back cover photography © Stefan Holm/iStock/Thinkstock

Library of Congress Cataloging-in-Publication Data

Holliday, Richard J. (Richard John), 1933– author.
    A holistic vet's prescription for a healthy herd : a guide to livestock nutrition, free-choice minerals, and holistic cattle care / Richard Holliday, DVM and Jim Helfter.
        pages cm
    Includes index.
    ISBN 978-1-60173-088-6 (print)
    ISBN 978-1-60173-089-3 (Kindle Mobi)
    ISBN 978-1-60173-090-9 (ePub)
    1. Cattle—Nutrition. 2. Minerals in animal nutrition. 3. Holistic veterinary medicine.
I. Helfter, Jim, author. II. Title. III. Title: Guide to livestock nutrition, free-choice minerals, and holistic cattle care.

SF203.H725   2014   636.2'083--dc23

2014036735

This work is dedicated to William D. "Bill" Johnson (1933–2008), a pioneer in holistic ruminant nutrition.

Building on the scientific work of Dr. William A. Albrecht, Bill was able to implement a comprehensive and workable approach to livestock mineral nutrition. Generations of livestock owners, coast to coast, thank him for his applied common sense.

Bill's philosophy in brief: No two animals have the same mineral needs, and no one bag of mineral meets all animal requirements.

Contents

Preface

Wild animals were balancing their own nutrient and mineral needs long before man came on the scene. In the wild, grazing animals have a large variety of plants to choose from and have little need for minerals beyond that which can be satisfied by the salt licks and mineral licks commonly found while roaming from one region to another.

With domestication came confinement and soil depletion, both of which limited the animals' nutritional choices. The nutritional wisdom of animals was subjugated to the so-called nutritional knowledge of man.

The purpose of this book is to show how we can improve animal health and well-being by allowing grazing animals to once again exercise their nutritional wisdom by self-selecting from a wide variety of minerals. This is not a book that examines different alternative animal treatments, nor is it filled with research data or esoteric formulas. It is, however, a compilation of knowledge, experience, and opinions garnered from many years of involvement in holistic veterinary medicine and animal nutrition. At all times our goal has been to share with the reader the idea that anyone can prove fundamental concepts of animal health by watching and learning from animals, who will share their secrets with us if we are attentive.

This book is dedicated to enabling readers to better appreciate their own powers of observation and thus free themselves from reliance on erroneous, bought-and-paid-for industrial or university research.

Holistic Animal Health and Nutrition

PART 1

1

....

The Evolution of a Holistic Veterinarian

I believe that a broad interest in soil conservation began in the 1930s as a result of the devastating Dust Bowl, when the shortcomings of that era's agricultural practices became apparent. This trend has continued on many fronts, and the most visible one at present is the organic movement. It is important to remember that organic is only one part of a much larger trend toward sustainable agriculture that is changing the very nature of farming here in the United States and in many other parts of the world as well. My evolution as a holistic veterinarian roughly paralleled this broader national movement.

In high school I read Louis Bromfield's books *Pleasant Valley* and *Malabar Farm*, in which he detailed his success in rebuilding worn-out farms near his boyhood home in Ohio. These books were my earliest exposure to alternative agriculture. They are still a good reference for anyone interested in soil conservation and the early history of at least one part of the natural farming movement.

During my undergraduate studies at the University of Missouri, I had the opportunity to study soils under the renowned Dr. William A. Albrecht. It was years later that I fully appreciated the importance of his work, that it takes healthy soils to make healthy crops and healthy crops to make healthy animals. His book *Soil Fertility and Animal Health* is a classic. Dr. Albrecht's influence and acceptance in the realm of sustainable or biological agriculture is greater now than while he was alive. One of his sayings was, "Study

Originally printed in the June 2007 issue of *The Progressive Dairyman*.

books and observe nature; if they do not agree, throw away the books." I have tried to follow this advice throughout my career, and it has paid huge dividends in insights and knowledge gained.

In vet school I was fortunate that most of my clinical instructors were former veterinary practitioners. They gave us a practicality in our approach to medicine that kept our minds open to anything that worked.

One of our large-animal ambulatory instructors was an elderly gentleman, previously retired from his own practice and then hired by the university when the veterinary program was started. His inquisitive mind was an inspiration to all his students. He would try any sort of treatment at least once before judging its worth. The results of some of these unorthodox remedies and therapies were at times astounding. He taught us to not be bound by tradition and not be afraid to try something new or to explore a new idea.

When I first became interested in holistic animal care, one of my "natural farming clients" had planted a large acreage of corn (maize) in a fertile river bottom area. We drove to an area where his cornfield joined his neighbor's. Everyone that farmed around him used chemical fertilizer, herbicides, and pesticides. He used only a trace mineral–rich gypsum (calcium sulfate) substance that was mined in Colorado. The corn on both lands was tall and green, but the plants in several rows around the perimeter of my client's field were severely damaged. He experienced little damage from insects or weeds, but the native deer would come from miles around to eat his organic corn, leaving his neighbor's crops untouched.

We did a taste test. The sap from his corn tasted sweet, almost like sugar cane. One row away, just across the fence, the sap was bland and had a bitter aftertaste. He then suggested that I notice the number of empty pesticide cans in the trash dumps on the farms where I made most of my sick animal vet calls and look for a correlation. I definitely spotted one. I have never forgotten his words, and I have seldom found them in error. He taught me two natural principles: animals can recognize and will seek out healthy nutrition if available, and there is an adverse relationship between heavy use of ag-chemicals and animal health.

The year 1940 saw the publication of *An Agricultural Testament* by Sir Albert Howard, an English researcher working in India to develop composting methods to increase soil fertility. He found that animals were healthier when fed highly nutritious feed grown on high-organic-matter soils. He reported that his work-oxen that fed on these "organically grown" feeds remained healthy even when directly exposed to foot-and-mouth disease.

Sir Albert's book is reputed to have been the impetus for J. I. Rodale to begin publication of the magazine *Organic Gardening and Farming*. This magazine was instrumental in popularizing the health benefits of organic farming for animals and humans alike. In the sixties and seventies it was our program guide as we tried to farm our small acreage organically and apply natural principles to our own health and that of our animals. It also inspired me to become more holistic in my vet practice. *Acres U.S.A.* is another national publication that has been a tremendous advocate for ecological agriculture for over thirty years. The founder, Charles Walters, was a pioneer in this field and wrote extensively on this subject.

In 1984 I became employed as a technical services veterinarian for a company that produces and markets colostrum whey–based animal health and nutrition products. For the last twenty-three years I've been able to apply holistic principles to various health problems as I consult with large and small organic and conventional dairymen across the country. In 1988 I witnessed the birth of the CROPP Cooperative, and I have been peripherally associated with its Organic Valley label ever since. In 1989 I took advanced training from the International Veterinary Acupuncture Society and became board certified in veterinary acupuncture. The study of five-thousand-year-old holistic medical technology added a whole new dimension to my understanding of health and disease.

When the Rodales first popularized the term "organic," it referred to the goal of building fertile, biologically active soils high in organic matter. At present, the emphasis of organic regulation seems to have shifted somewhat from soil building to restricting the use of prohibited substances. The U.S. Department of Agriculture (USDA) defines the requirements to qualify as organic and the National Organic Standards Board (NOSB) ensures compliance with some of the more important natural principles. It is interesting to note that while organic-certified dairies are regulated by the government, all dairies are subject to the constraints imposed by natural principles and the innate nature of the cow.

2

·················

Some Thoughts on Holistic or Alternative Veterinary Medicine

It is a difficult task to briefly describe holistic or "alternative" veterinary medicine. The dictionary defines "holistic" as concerning wholes or complete systems rather than parts or divisions, while "alternative" describes something existing or functioning outside the established cultural, social, or economic system. Both definitions are correct, but neither adequately addresses the wide variations within the realm of holistic veterinary medicine as practiced today.

The range of alternative therapies is immense: acupuncture, herbs, homeopathy, refined colostrum products, microbial products (lactobacillus and yeasts), mega-vitamins, radionics, and many other natural products and procedures. The list goes on and on, and I apologize if I've left out someone's favorite therapy. Most are useful and generally effective alternatives to the drugs, hormones, and antibiotics commonly used in veterinary medicine today.

A HOLISTIC PRACTITIONER

I believe that the distinguishing characteristic of holistic practitioners is the way they approach problems—in short, the way they think. A true holistic veterinarian not only looks at the patient as an integrated unit but also views the patient in the context of the whole ecosystem in which it lives. In this regard, a sick animal is not only a patient to be treated but also a symptom of a sick farm. Both patients need help. Any remedial action must include what is necessary for the immediate relief of the animal as well as a critical assessment of the long-term effects of the chosen therapy on the patient and the environment. Part of the treatment must also be the removal or reduction of predisposing factors.

A holistic practitioner should also be well-versed in several treatment modalities and be able to pick the most appropriate ones for any situation. In some cases this might even include the judicious use of antibiotics, if the need is really indicated and if it has a reasonably good chance of success.

Finally, a true holistic practitioner should emphasize holistic animal health management (proactive) rather than any kind of treatment (reactive), whether holistic or conventional.

It should be noted that the terms holistic and alternative are not interchangeable. For example: an acupuncturist may be practicing alternative medicine, but if he only treats symptoms and does not search for the cause or other useful therapies, he is probably not a holistic practitioner. A fine distinction perhaps, but a significant one.

ADVANTAGES AND DISADVANTAGES

To me, the greatest advantage to the holistic approach is that it works! In the hands of an experienced practitioner, most holistic/alternative treatments have as good as or better success rates than conventional therapy. I think this is true because holistic practitioners attempt to find and treat the cause of the illness, not just the symptoms.

There are many other advantages to holistic medicine: less pollution, fewer side effects, and especially the fact that holistic medicine follows the old medical axiom, "Do no harm." This advice seems to have been lost or overlooked in much of the United States, as evidenced by the recent report that pharmaceutical drugs are now either the fourth or sixth leading cause of death.*

Unfortunately, several factors have slowed public acceptance of holistic medicine. The sale and use of natural products do not generate the huge profits necessary to buy researchers, lobbyists, and politicians as does the sale of antibiotics and pharmaceuticals. Thus we have little credibility in

---

* Donald W. Light, "Risky Drugs: Why the FDA Can't be Trusted," Harvard University Edmond J. Safra Research Lab, 2013, http://www.ethics.harvard.edu/lab/blog/312-risky -drugs.

some circles because we do not have research to back up our empirical observations. Because so few schools teach these advanced concepts, there are not enough qualified practitioners, although the number is growing. Those that do engage in holistic practice are often subjected to harassment by government agencies.

The biggest disadvantage is that most people tend to use holistic treatments for the wrong reasons and at the wrong times! They will turn to alternative treatments only as a last resort when everything conventional medicine has to offer has failed. Usually by this time the patient is in advanced stages of the disease and also suffering from the side effects of all the prescribed drugs they have used. When the alternative approach also fails, and it usually does in this situation, the patient gives up on the entire concept and never realizes that the alternative treatment might have worked had they used the right product or technique at the right time. Unfortunately, this apparent "failure" provides more evidence for the pharmaceutical/medical complex to ridicule and condemn the entire concept of holistic medicine.

THE FOCUS OF HOLISTIC ANIMAL HUSBANDRY

The success of the holistic approach requires a change in public perspective and the development of a holistic outlook towards livestock management and disease control. It is not as simple as merely substituting a "natural" alternate therapy for a "toxic" drug. The principles behind the success of holistic therapy go much deeper than the characteristics or source of the medication.

Conventional veterinary medicine is primarily concerned with the *treatment* of sick animals. Even if successful, the loss of life and production added to the cost of treatment makes this approach by far the most expensive.

Veterinarians also emphasize disease *prevention*. Herd health checks and vaccination programs fall into this category. As essential as these procedures are, the outlook is still toward preventing disease. Vaccinations may increase resistance against a specific organism but do little to elevate the animal's vitality to the level of health enhancement. Typical of this category are herds or flocks where the animals are not really sick or showing symptoms but are not really well and productive either.

A third concept, usually neglected by conventional veterinary practitioners, is that of *health enhancement through holistic management*. Everything possible is done to raise health and vitality to the highest level. All management practices are evaluated on the basis of their effects on the vitality of each animal in the herd. Strict attention is given to providing superlative nutrition. Insofar as possible, all environmental stress factors are eliminated. Water is checked for nitrates or other toxins. Housing and ventilation are maintained at optimum levels. Any equipment with which the animals come into contact is properly maintained and adjusted. There are literally hundreds of other environmental factors that impact animal health, and they all must be considered. When animals are maintained at a high level of vitality, their resistance to disease is much higher. Health enhancement is much more profitable than either treatment or prevention.

SOME THOUGHTS ABOUT STRESS

Stress is known to lower immune function and may be the primary factor that sets the stage for animal disease. There are four categories of stress.

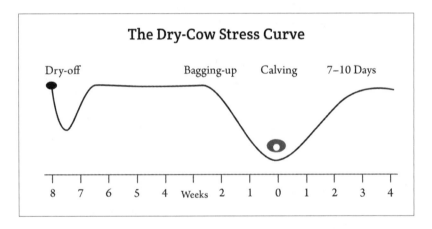

1. Environmental or physical stress, such as faulty nutrition, bad water, lack of sanitation, poorly designed and maintained equipment, unsuitable habitat, etc. Good management has some influence on most of these but cannot control all of them. For example, weather cannot be controlled, but the negative effects of the weather can be mitigated with proper housing.
2. Physiological stress, usually associated with reproduction and lactation. We can minimize some of the effects of this type, but we cannot totally

eliminate it. See the Dry Cow Stress Curve as an example of physiological stress.

3. Psychological stress may occur when weaning, changing groups, establishing a new pecking order, etc. This type of stress can be held to an acceptable level with good management.

4. Stress caused by an inability to fulfill inherent live tendencies. For example, horses like to run. Cows are herd animals and do best in a group setting. Animals will also become stressed when forced to eat feedstuffs incompatible with their evolutionary origins—for example, feeding dairy cows a 50 percent grain ration.

All animals vary in their ability to accommodate stress. Some differences are due to inheritance: species, breed, and sex. Others are associated with the individual's history of health and disease. Older animals do not accommodate stress as well as younger ones do. A young animal that suffers an episode of severe scours/pneumonia may survive, grow, and appear thrifty even though some irreversible damage to heart, lungs, and intestinal lining may forever impair the animal's ability to pump blood and absorb oxygen and nutrients. Under stress this animal will probably show earlier and more severe symptoms than others in the same group that did not go through the sickness.

Stresses are cumulative. A small stress has a greater effect in an animal already carrying a big stress load than it has in another, relatively stress-free animal.

THE VITALITY CHART

Over many years, I have developed a graph that allows me focus my thinking and helps me keep the various aspects of health and disease in proper perspective. Any animal's relative health status can be plotted on this graph. Since this vitality chart also seems useful to illustrate certain principles of holistic thought, I would like to share it with you and will use it as the basis for this section and for almost all future discussions of health and disease.

On the chart, note that the "vitality" line on the left side (looks like a thermometer) runs from perfect health to dead. I purposefully do not assign any numbers because the positions are variable and I'd prefer to think in terms of relationships rather than absolutes. I doubt anyone ever attains perfect health, but "dead" is all too common.

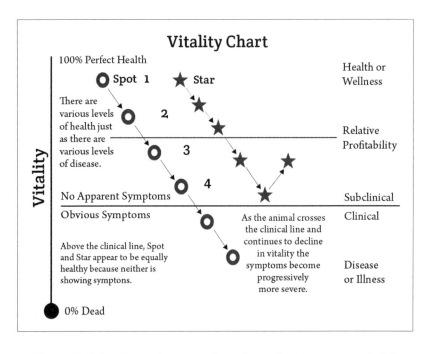

The profitability line indicates a relative loss of production, profitability, or performance. The "clinical line" by definition separates healthy animals from sick animals based solely on the presence or absence of symptoms. These lines are actually wide gray areas, and their positions are arbitrary and quite variable. Judgment depends a great deal on how well the herdsman relates to and observes his animals.

If an animal progressively declines from good health to sickness or even death (going straight down the left side of the chart), it will first cross the "profitability line" as it becomes less productive and then the "clinical line" when it begins to show symptoms of disease. These symptoms may be mild at first—"a little off"—gradually increasing in severity until "dead" (see Vitality Chart). We know and accept that there are differing levels of illness, but our management decisions frequently seem to be based on the premise that "Star" is just as healthy as "Spot." We all know that different levels of health do exist, but in practice we tend to overlook this because "Spot" and "Star" both look equally healthy even though there is a great difference in their respective vitality. Production records and breeding records are a great aid to identify those animals that have lost productivity but are not yet showing symptoms of any disease.

Let's compare the reactions of "Spot" and "Star," both living relatively stress-free lives and possessing a high level of vitality (position 1 on the chart). If something happens to their ration and they are subjected to nutritional stress, they will probably both decline in vitality to position 2. Notice that Spot was affected more severely, possibly because she suffered a grave illness when young (as discussed earlier). Both still appear to be healthy and productive but some of their "reserve" is used up.

Adding another stress causes both to slip down to position 3. Star is still doing well, but now Spot has dropped under the profitability line. She shows no clinical symptoms but performance or production testing may indicate problems. In a dairy animal this could be evidenced by lowered production, a change in somatic cell count (SCC), or an impairment of breeding efficiency.

Add one more stress and Spot and Star fall to position 4, both below the profitability line. Spot is dangerously close to the clinical line but still shows no obvious symptoms, although a really close observer might see mild symptoms developing.

As one last insult, let's expose both of them to a pathogenic bacteria capable of causing disease. Both suffer the same loss of vitality from this exposure. Star dips in vitality but does not go clinical. She is able to overcome the infection because she had some resistance left. Spot drops over the line and begins to show symptoms. Conventional medicine would diagnose the bacteria as the "cause" of her disease.

This example is obviously oversimplified to illustrate a principle, but does beg the question: "In this example, did the germs cause the disease?" Or would it be more accurate to ask: "Did the bacteria trigger a disease in an animal that was already suffering from stress-induced low vitality?" I go with the trigger theory. The deciding factor was not the presence or absence of a disease organism, but the presence or absence of a strong immune system. Obviously, microorganisms do vary in their ability to cause disease, and a highly pathogenic organism may be able to cause disease in relatively stress-free animals. These epidemics, however, are probably not as costly in the long run as the day-to-day losses incurred by common infections.

I think we give germs way too much weight as the cause of problems. My guess is that a germ can't tell if an animal is dead or alive but if an animal is so stressed out that it "tastes" dead to the bacteria, they immediately begin the recycling process. In a dead animal we call it decomposition; in a live animal we call it disease. In the grand scheme of things, the bugs are probably only doing the job assigned to them. If one really believes that germs cause disease, then, by that same logic, they must believe that flies cause garbage.

Some Observations Based on the Chart

- Let's go back to poor old Spot's predicament. We could give her some antibiotics and hopefully kill enough germs to get her back up over the clinical line. Or we could treat her with herbs or homeopathy and probably help her enough to shut off the symptoms. But, unless we eliminate the stresses that put her at the susceptible level in the first place, we have really only applied a big Band-Aid!
- Timing is critically important. If you start treatment early, a mild treatment has a greater chance of getting results. If this is not successful, you still have time to escalate to a more heroic treatment. Some conventional dairymen overlook the importance of timing when their hopes for a spontaneous recovery lead them to withhold treatment of sick animals until the last possible moment in order to minimize the economic loss of discarded milk or meat. A holistic treatment does not have this disadvantage and can be used anytime.
- Generally speaking, the closer to the top of the chart we recognize a problem and begin to correct it, the lower the cost.
- If healing and/or health occur at all, it is a function of the natural inclination of the animal to be healthy. Drugs, from whatever source derived, only aid this natural process.
- Just because an animal shows no symptoms does not mean it's healthy.
- The final stress that triggers symptoms is usually not the primary cause of the illness. For example, bacteria may trigger mastitis but the real cause may be nutritional deficiencies or other stresses.

A QUIZ

Whether you are already following holistic principles or aspire to do so, you should be able to answer these questions. If you can't answer them, you have some homework to do.

1. Is the feed ration adequate with no excesses, deficiencies, or toxins? Were the feeds grown on fertile soil with little or no chemical contamination? Do the animals have the opportunity to fulfill and balance their mineral needs? Are the feed ingredients appropriate to the species, type, and age of the animal?

2. Is the water pure? Has it been checked for nitrates and other harmful chemicals? What is the actual nitrate level in the water? Do you drink from the same water supply as the animals? Does the water taste good to you?

3. Are there any harmful electrical or electromagnetic influences on the premise? Do you ever receive mild electrical shocks when working in the area where the animals are kept?

4. If used, is milking equipment properly maintained and adjusted?

5. Are all procedures involving the animals such as milking, vaccinating, and routine surgery carried out in a timely and sanitary manner?

6. Do your animals have a clean, dry, well-ventilated environment when confined? Can you kneel down in the pens without getting wet knees? Is breathing uncomfortable or unpleasant to you when breathing at the same distance above the ground as the animal breathes in air?

7. Is there any evidence of mold, mycotoxins, or aflatoxins in the feed? Some are not apparent until symptoms occur; have you checked?

3

How Nutrition Can Affect Animal Health

In 1951 I had the good fortune to study the rudiments of soil science at the University of Missouri under the late Dr. William Albrecht. I must confess that at the time I took his course, I did not fully appreciate the correlation between soil fertility and animal health. I wanted to get on with the real veterinarian's job of treating sick animals. It was only after I had completed my "animal disease" education in veterinary school and began to receive my "animal health" education from some dedicated organic farmer clients that I came back to Albrecht's work and finally began to understand his wisdom.

His book *Soil Fertility and Animal Health** is a classic and should be required reading for anyone aspiring to be a holistic herdsman. As one could guess from the title, his premise is that it takes fertile, healthy soil to grow healthy, nutritious crops to sustain healthy, productive animals or people. Incidentally, soil vitality and crop or feed vitality as well as animal vitality can be plotted on the vitality chart discussed in the previous chapter.

Stated another way, an animal can only be as healthy as the feed it eats, and the feed can only be as healthy as the soil upon which it was grown. For the soil to be healthy, it must be highly fertile, adequately watered, highly mineralized, biologically active, and free from herbicides, insecticides, or

---

* Dr. William Albrecht, *The Albrecht Papers*, ed. Charles Walters, vol. 2, *Soil Fertility and Animal Health* (Austin, TX: Acres U.S.A., 1975).

other chemical toxins. Within the broad framework of this concept, in this chapter I would like to illustrate four main points:

- Good nutrition can prevent disease.
- Good nutrition can cure disease.
- Nature is a better judge of nutrition than nutritionists.
- Healthy production is the most profitable.

GOOD NUTRITION CAN PREVENT DISEASE . . . MOST OF THE TIME, BUT NOT ALWAYS!

Another candidate for a required reading list is the book *An Agricultural Testament* by Sir Albert Howard, originally published in 1940.* Sir Albert was formerly the director of the Institute of Plant Industry in Indore, India, and the British Agricultural Adviser to States in Central India and Pajutana. *An Agricultural Testament* is the summation of decades of his work to improve soil fertility and plant and animal health by composting agricultural residues and returning them to the soil.

His work is credited as one of the sparks that inspired J. I. Rodale to begin publication of the great magazine *Organic Gardening and Farming* and also the inspiration for the Haughley Experiment—the first scientific comparative study of organic farming and conventional chemical-based agriculture. Most of Sir Albert's work is related to soil fertility and the intricacies of composting, but I would like to quote a paragraph from his *The Soil and Health* that forever changed the way I looked at animal health and disease.

> My work animals were most carefully selected and everything was done to provide them with suitable housing and with fresh green fodder, silage, and grain, all produced from fertile land. I was naturally intensely interested in watching the reaction of these well-chosen and well-fed oxen to diseases like rinderpest, septicaemia, and foot-and-mouth disease which frequently devastated the countryside. None of my animals were segregated; none were inoculated; they frequently came in contact with diseased stock. As my small farm-yard at Pusa was only separated by a low hedge from one of the large cattle-sheds on the Pusa estate, in which outbreaks of foot-and-mouth disease often occurred, I

---

* Sir Albert Howard, *An Agricultural Testament* (New York: Oxford University Press, 1940).

have several times seen my oxen rubbing noses with foot-and-mouth cases. Nothing happened. The healthy well-fed animals reacted to this disease exactly as suitable varieties of crops, when properly grown, did to insect and fungus pests—no infection took place.

Once my mind was opened to the possibility that good nutrition could prevent disease, I found evidence of it almost every place I looked.

GOOD NUTRITION CAN CURE DISEASE . . . OFTEN, BUT NOT ALWAYS!

Farmer and environmentalist Eugene M. Poirot wrote a book called *Our Margin of Life* that details his experiences in the restoration of soils and the health benefits to animals fed crops grown on high-vitality soils.* His son-in-law, a veterinarian who practiced in the same town as I did, confirmed the accuracy of this account, here quoted from Poirot's book.

> Once Bang's disease, which causes abortion, was so serious, and the blood test showed so high a percentage of infected cows, that the entire herd was threatened with liquidation. Fourteen years later, another test of all animals, including both the old infected cows and their offspring, more than four hundred head, failed to show a single reactor or suspect. When Bang's disease is transmitted to humans by cows or their products it is called undulant fever. In this case it was controlled at the soil level in some yet unknown way, long before it had a chance to reach a human as undulant fever.
>
> A significant part of this story is that early in the restoration period this disease was eradicated by blood-testing cows and selling all reactors and suspects. The herd was clean for a period of three years. Then the infection hit again in January, when an immediate blood test disclosed only six head of reactors or suspects. These were sold at once, but by June the infection had reached eighty percent of the cows!

---

* Eugene M. Poirot, *Our Margin of Life* (Raytown, MS: Acres U.S.A., 1978).

So none were sold, and soil restoration was continued. In two years calf crops became normal again.

Later, blood testing became required by law, but no reactors or suspects were found in any of the tests, nor has the disease reappeared after thirty-five years, even though all animals are offspring of infected cows, born on once infected pastures and living in an area where Bang's disease was present on other farms before blood testing eradicated it.

I don't know how to "cure" these many diseases—but Mother Nature does. That is why I like to give her the "tools" and keep her on my side.

NATURE IS A BETTER JUDGE OF NUTRITION THAN NUTRITIONISTS . . . IF THE PROPER CHOICES ARE AVAILABLE!

My good friend and client Carl lived down the highway about three miles from our home. He was a good farmer and dairyman who milked about thirty cows. My vet calls to his place were mostly for routine jobs like dehorning or vaccinating with an occasional milk fever or dystocia. His cows were well cared for and healthy. For many years he supplied our family with fresh milk right from the bulk tank. One year inclement weather made planting and harvesting hay and grain crops a great gamble, with the result that feedstuffs that fall and winter looked good but had low nutritional value. By late winter Carl consulted with me about two seemingly unrelated problems. One, his cattle were eating almost two pounds of a mixed mineral per head per day! Two, about ten days before they were due to calve, his heifers would abort a live calf. The calf, with some care, would live, but despite all we could do the heifer would die within two or three days. After the third one in a row had died, I did what every smart vet would do: I passed the buck and sent a dying heifer to the university vet school for autopsy. Their diagnosis came back as *starvation*! Carl took good care of his animals and was feeding them almost all they could eat. This diagnosis was like an insult to Carl and difficult for either of us to accept. We could have accepted a diagnosis of malnutrition because of the poor crops that year, but starvation seemed a little too harsh.

We then turned our attention to the mineral consumption problem. Available in the area at that time was a "cafeteria" mineral program in which

Hey, Doc, Waddaya Got for Cows Eating Dirt?

A few years ago, I posed this question at several dairy seminars in the Midwest: "Do your animals chew on wood or eat dirt if they have the chance?" A few said their cows would chew on wood. Almost all indicated their cows would eat dirt if available. One fellow said that he had to haul in dirt around the foundations of his buildings to replace the soil his cows had eaten over a period of years. Strangely enough, a few even told of their cows licking or drinking from urine puddles if they could get to them. As bad as that sounds, it is even more alarming when conventional opinion regards this eating behavior as being almost normal because it is so common. It's the "everybody's doing it, so it must be okay" syndrome. And it may be "normal," in the sense that it is appropriate, compensatory behavior for animals forced to subsist on a mineral-deficient ration. Eating dirt and other abnormal appetites are attempts to secure some vital element or attain some nutritive balance that is not otherwise present in their diet. It should be considered a warning signal that something is amiss in the ration.

To examine the problem from a holistic viewpoint, let's go back in time and look at the effect of domestication on today's dairy cattle. Most authorities agree that primitive cattle or aurochs (*Bos primigenius taurus*) were first domesticated about eight thousand years ago. Before domestication, cattle lived a lifestyle similar to that of bison in the American West. They were free to roam over wide, naturally fertile areas. Specific imbalances of soil in one area would be offset by excesses or adequacy of the same element in other areas. A multitude of different plants were available. Many plants had the ability to absorb and concentrate different minerals and trace minerals, giving the grazers even greater nutrient options. Thus, over a period of time the aurochs could seek out and obtain balanced mineral and nutritional needs. Predators strengthened the genetic pool by culling the weak and unfit.

It's a lot different today. Dairy cattle have been genetically modified to produce at levels never intend by nature, increasing their need for minerals. Ever more restrictive confinement limits their ability to seek out and consume adequate diets. In a natural grazing situation herbivores probably had hundreds of different plants from which to choose. Today they are limited to six or less: grass, alfalfa, corn, soybeans, cottonseed, and maybe some oats or barley. Seeds and grains in the amounts currently fed are detrimental to dairy cow health. Cows are ruminants and need a high-forage diet!

Crop quality has declined. Every crop harvested or animal removed from a farm or ranch takes with it a finite amount of life-supporting nutrients. Major elements can be replaced, but it is difficult to restore a natural balance that includes high organic matter, adequate trace minerals, and vibrant biological life. Intensive NPK fertilization results in higher yields at the expense of nutritive values and mineral content in the crops.

"AVERAGE" IS A MYTH

A total mixed ration (TMR) is the industry standard feeding strategy that purports to provide, in one total mix, all the nutrition required by the "average" cow in the group. This concept fails to consider the individuality of each animal's nutrient requirements. No two animals have the same needs. Variables such as breed, age, pregnancy, stage of lactation, weather, season of the year, and others have a marked influence on the need for mineral supplementation. With a TMR probably no one animal will get exactly what it needs. A few may get pretty close, but many will be lacking in some nutrients while others will have excesses. This imbalance limits their production, eventually depresses their immune response, and ultimately may result in various herd health problems. Eating dirt, if it's available, is their way of responding to these imbalances.

Unfortunately, mainstream nutritionists tend to downplay the ability of animals to balance their nutritional needs. Anyone who doubts that cattle can make valid nutritional choices needs to watch cows graze in a mixed pasture. They do not just mow grass like a lawn mower, but pick and choose each mouthful. They avoid eating the bright green grass surrounding "cow pies" in the pasture but will search the fencerows for weeds that concentrate various essential trace minerals. Given the chance, they will balance their nutritional needs during each feeding period.

If your cows are eating dirt or if you just want to experiment; give your cows a chance to participate in their own diet formulation. Provide separate free-choice sources of these six items: salt, bentonite, bicarbonate, a basic mixed mineral with a 2:1 calcium-phosphorus ratio, one with a 1:2 calcium-phosphorus ratio, and kelp. Cows with rumen acidosis will prefer bicarbonate or bentonite. The separate sources of calcium and phosphorus allow them to adjust that critical ratio. If the animals lack trace minerals, they may also eat a lot of kelp. If kelp consumption remains high, you may want to provide separate sources of some of the trace minerals. There are commercial companies that provide a broad range of separate free-choice minerals and trace minerals.

We should use our nutritional knowledge to formulate dairy rations, but also rely on the nutritional wisdom of animals to fine-tune their individual needs. It doesn't hurt to have two opinions, one from your nutritionist's computer and one from the real experts—your cows. I will leave it to you to decide which one is the more reliable.

Originally printed in the October 2007 issue of *The Progressive Dairyman.*

each mineral was fed separately on the theory that each animal could then eat only what it needed to balance its own needs. Carl decided to try this program. His mineral feeder was in the middle of his cow lot, and he had to carry each bag of minerals through the lot to empty into the feeder. Things went well for the first few trips, and then suddenly several of the normally docile cows suddenly surrounded him, tore a bag of mineral from his arms. chewed open the bag, and greedily consumed every bit of the mineral, the bag, and even some mud and muck where the mineral had spilled out—astounding behavior for a bunch of tame dairy cows!

What was in the bag, you ask? A source of the trace mineral, zinc. During the next several days, they ate several bags of this zinc source while completely ignoring all other minerals. Gradually they began eating normal amounts of the regular mineral once again. From that day on his heifers calved normally and things gradually returned to normal.

Apparently, the difficult growing season has resulted in crops that were deficient in zinc or perhaps high in zinc antagonists. The basic mineral mix had a small amount of zinc in it, but to get the zinc they needed, the cows had to consume large amounts. This gave them too much calcium. Calcium interferes with zinc absorption, which in turn increased their need for zinc (see chart 3.1). Even though their quest for zinc impelled them to eat the mixed mineral, every mouthful they took increased the imbalance. Inevitably, symptoms began to show up in the most vulnerable group: young heifers, still growing and in the last stages of pregnancy. Finally they just gave up and checked out, all for want of a few grams of zinc. The decrease in feed conversion associated with zinc deficiencies coupled with the poor-quality feed would result in malnutrition even when feed intake appeared to be adequate. I realize that other secondary factors may have been involved here, but the main factor was a zinc deficiency as evidenced by the remission of symptoms when zinc was supplied. (See "Zinc" sidebar).

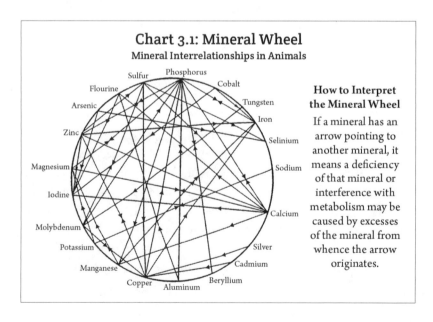

Chart 3.1: Mineral Wheel
Mineral Interrelationships in Animals

How to Interpret the Mineral Wheel

If a mineral has an arrow pointing to another mineral, it means a deficiency of that mineral or interference with metabolism may be caused by excesses of the mineral from whence the arrow originates.

Carl had done as good a job as he could with the knowledge that was available at the time. When the essential ingredients were finally provided so that the animals could make their own choice, they picked out what they needed to regain their health. For me this incident epitomizes the concept that, given the chance, animals can balance rations better than computers or nutritionists can.

Many nutritionists tend to discount the ability of animals to balance their rations, asserting that by the time they feel the need to eat a certain item they are already in a deficient state. From their point of view, I suppose they have a point. The fallacy in their reasoning may be that they expect the animal to choose for the level of production that man desires while the animal chooses only what it needs to be healthy.

HEALTHY PRODUCTION IS THE MOST PROFITABLE . . . IN THE LONG-TERM IF NOT IN THE SHORT-TERM!

Many years ago I was associated with a feed company that formulated and sold premixes for dairy cattle. It was a good feed, based on "natural" ingredients and principles. Many of the users commented on the superb health experienced by the animals on this program: better reproduction, less mastitis, low cull rate, healthy calves, low vet bills, etc.

The downside was that production, although profitable, did not reach the high levels they had come to expect when feeding a more "conventional" ration designed mainly to increase production. Many dairymen who switched to such a feeding program often saw their production increase dramatically.

Unfortunately, in most of these cases, it was not very long before problems began creeping back into the herd: cows did not come in heat like they should, conception rate went down. There were more cases of mastitis, calves did not do as well, vet expense increased, and more cows began leaving the herd for health reasons. Eventually even production began to slide. The short-term higher production promised by the conventional feed had been gained only at the long-term expense of lowered herd health, illustrating that old saying, "There's no such thing as a free lunch."

There does seem to be a level at which animals can maintain health and have profitable production. The animals on the "natural" feeding program had achieved this happy state, and the overall financial benefit associated with good health more than overcame the slightly lower production and

Zinc

Stress (including birthing) appears to increase the zinc requirement of animals.

Zinc is required for the incorporation of cystine into keratin and thus plays an important role in maintaining hoof, horn, and skin integrity.

Zinc plays an important role in wound healing, immune function, and disease resistance. Some studies indicate that the first symptoms of zinc deficiency are a decrease in immune function and a decrease in feed conversion.

Zinc plays a role in vitamin A transport and utilization and appears to play a role in vitamin E absorption. Reproductive performance after parturition (birthing) improves with both zinc and vitamin E supplementation in late pregnancy.

High calcium and iron intake (including calcium and iron in water) will increase animals' zinc requirement.

Deficiency symptoms may include general listlessness, poor growth, stiff joints and unthrifty appearance, hair loss, general dermatitis of head and neck, and failure of wounds to heal properly.

slightly higher feed costs. When a herd like this is switched to a "conventional" program concerned mostly with high production, the increased production and slightly lower feed costs usually do not make up for the increased costs of poor health.

SEE EVERYTHING YOU LOOK AT!

The previous experiences, along with many others, confirmed for me what Dr. Albrecht, Sir Albert, and Mr. Poirot had discovered years before. Building on the foundation they had provided, I subsequently learned a lot about nutrition and animal health just by paying attention to what animals ate and the effects on their health. You, too, can prove these things to yourself by doing the same.

4

Let Your Animals Teach You Nutrition

I believe that a ruminant's tongue is the finest nutritional analytical laboratory in the world. Many experiences over the years have taught me to trust in the natural inclination of animals to seek out the best nutrition they can find and to know instantly when they have found it. Early on in my veterinary practice in Missouri, my office was next to a feed store that carried a line of free-choice minerals and trace minerals. I didn't pay much attention to that concept until one day the salesman for the company invited himself out to my small farm to educate me on the benefits of his mineral program for my small group of horses and beef cattle. He suggested putting out a dozen or more separate minerals. That seemed like overkill to me, especially since I already put out some mixed minerals every once in awhile and the livestock usually had a trace-mineral salt block available. Being persistent, this fellow even rigged up several small separate compartments in the ends of a couple of my existing feed-bunks. He filled each one with a different mineral. He asked me to watch and see what happened. I was amazed. After only one day, it was apparent that the stock had sampled everything, the phosphorus source was licked clean, and a lot of calcium was gone. I kept the boxes full. Though erratic at first, consumption gradually tapered off but never ceased entirely. Any new animals added to the group would spend their first few days at the mineral box. Some would gorge on calcium and some on phosphorus. Most would sample all the minerals to one extent or another. Once they reached satiety, the total consumption was negligible unless pasture or weather conditions changed or when feeding hay or grain from a new or different source.

Anyone who doubts that cattle can make valid nutritional choices only needs to watch a cow graze in a mixed pasture. As I've said, they do not just mow grass like a lawn mower but pick and choose each mouthful and, if given the opportunity, will balance their nutritional needs during each feeding period. They judiciously avoid eating the bright green grass surrounding cow pies in the pasture but will search the fencerows for weeds because many concentrate various essential trace minerals. Let me relate a few examples to help you discover similar occurrences in your own animals.

As I related in chapter 1, when I was first becoming interested in holistic animal care one of my good "natural farming" clients took me on an impromptu field trip. We drove to an area where his cornfield joined his neighbor's. Both fields were basically the same as to soil type, variety, and stage of growth. His neighbor's corn was tall with dark green undamaged leaves. Kenny's corn was just about as tall and green but the plants in several rows around the perimeter of his field were severely damaged. He explained. "My neighbor uses all the modern chemical fertilizers, herbicides, and insecticides. I use only naturally occurring soil amendments like manure, lime, gypsum, and rock phosphate. Deer will walk through miles of 'chemical' corn without taking a bite and then feast on my crops because they taste better."

I have seen cattle escape from their pens, wander past fields of lush-looking "chemical" corn, and then, right to the row, begin to eat plants that were being grown according to natural principles.

I have seen swine that were accustomed to eating organic corn literally stop eating for two or three days until hunger finally drove them to begin eating a new batch of feed containing conventionally grown corn of inferior quality.

In their natural state, American bison roamed over thousands of miles of range and thus had access to naturally occurring minerals from a variety of soil types. A "buffalo" rancher in the upper Midwest must confine his herd to a few hundred acres. To duplicate as near as possible their former range of mineral choices, he provides continuous year-round access to twelve different free-choice minerals. The animals' consumption varies greatly, sometimes on a day-to-day basis, depending on the season, the weather, and the quality of the other feeds available. His animals are extremely healthy and productive.

Finally, one last example showing that ruminants can instantaneously detect minute changes in forage quality: Research from England indicates that grazing cows prefer clover during the day and grasses during the evening because sugar levels are highest in grass late in the day.*

Mainstream nutritionists tend to downplay this ability of an animal to balance its nutritional needs, possibly because they spend more time watching computer screens than observing the eating habits of the animals. I admit that this ability does not apply to all situations and to every type of feed. Some feed items (grain and concentrates) may be so tasty that most animals would overeat if fed free choice. Other ingredients are so unpalatable that voluntary consumption may not meet their requirements. Any attempt to increase the consumption of any one item by adding flavorings only seems to compound the problem. Nevertheless, this natural trait can be used to improve animal health and nutrition. And, in fact, there are many successful commercial suppliers of free-choice-mineral feeding programs wherein the major components are fed separately.

No prepared ration can match the exact needs of every animal or group of animals. In any given group being fed the same ration, some will get about what they need, some will get too much, and some will get too little. This is especially true of mineral components. For example, to provide trace minerals, most nutritionists disregard any trace minerals that may already be present in the feed and add a trace mineral package that provides the total trace mineral requirements. In theory, this assures that adequate amounts will be present. However, it does not address the possibility of interference caused by any excess thus created (see the mineral wheel chart in chapter 3).

A SELF-FED MINERAL PROGRAM

If you really want an education in mineral nutrition, and want to give your animals a chance to balance their own mineral requirements, try this program. Partition off your mineral feeder and provide the following in *separate* compartments on a continuous, free-choice basis.

---

* Research directly relating to preference of and production from ryegrass or clover in pure stands or in mixtures is found in C. J. Phillips and N. L. James, "The Effects of Including White Clover in Perennial Ryegrass Swards and the Height of Mixed Swards on the Milk Production, Sward Selection and Ingestive Behaviour of Dairy Cows," British Society of Animal Science, *Journal of Animal Science* 67 (1988): 195–202.

1. A mineral mix that is high in calcium with little or no phosphorus. You could use ground limestone (calcium carbonate), oyster shell flour, or combinations.
2. A mineral mix high in phosphorus with little or no calcium.
3. Loose salt (not block salt), the more unrefined the better.
4. Kelp, a rich source of all trace minerals and iodine.

Providing calcium and phosphorus separately allows the animals to maintain the critical calcium-to-phosphorus ratio.

SOME ADDITIONAL OPTIONS

Supplemental magnesium and potassium may not be necessary in all areas, but it doesn't hurt to make a feed-grade source available and see what happens.

Magnesium oxide and magnesium sulfate are common sources. They can be mixed with salt to improve palatability so long as a separate source of plain salt is also available. An alternative is to provide dolomite limestone that contains magnesium carbonate as well as calcium carbonate.

In many areas, potassium is already adequate or excessive. Potassium chloride or potassium bicarbonate is commonly used in commercial mixes to supply this mineral.

Sulfur is often deficient. Elemental sulfur can be provided free choice or mixed with salt.

Copper and zinc are often lacking and can be provided by mixing either copper sulfate or zinc sulfate with salt.

Baking soda or sodium bicarbonate free choice may be beneficial, especially if a lot of grain is being fed.

If not already present in some of the other mixes, provide a source of vitamins A, D, and E and some B vitamins.

At first, put out only small amounts and watch closely what they eat. More than likely, your animals will show a preference for one or two items, indicating a need. If your current ration is well balanced, they probably will not eat much. Even so, leave it out for them and watch what happens to the consumption patterns over time when pasture conditions change or when feeding hay or grain from a new or different source. I have seen daily changes in mineral preferences for no discernible reason.

Avoid sudden changes to the ration. If they seem to grossly overeat any one item, it may be prudent to partially limit that item for a week or so to let them catch up gradually.

If possible, avoid mineral mixes that are flavored to increase palatability.

If you are already feeding a complete ration with minerals added, do not change the ration. Use this program as an add-on, free-choice, monitoring system to let the animals tell you what they think of your ability as a nutritionist. This allows us to use our science and computers to at least get close to a balanced ration and still provide a way for the animals to fine-tune for their individual needs.

If you are not comfortable compounding your own separate mineral mixes, contact Advanced Biological Concepts in Osco, Illinois.* They have a sample kit containing twelve different minerals and trace minerals to be fed separately. In the long run it is probably more economical and safer to buy from a commercial source than undergo the hassle of doing it yourself.

SOME THOUGHTS

- If you are growing crops for your animals, farm organically or as close to it as you possibly can. If you buy your feed, try to find organically grown feed or feed that has been grown on fertile soil with a minimum of chemical inputs.
- From time to time, test some of your feed, especially if you buy feed or if you suspect feed-related problems. The lab test may quickly identify gross excesses or deficiencies in the feed and thus enable you to make adjustments before problems occur. It does not hurt to have two opinions, one from the lab and one from the consumers, your animals. I will leave it to you to decide which one is the more reliable.
- Don't forget that even with the best feeds malnutrition can still be an issue if the ration is not balanced and the ingredients are not appropriate to the species, age, and purpose of the animals being fed.
- Excess protein is often more common than a protein deficiency and can be more damaging. Do not add sources of non-protein nitrogen (NPNs) like urea or ammonia compounds to the ration. Test your feeds and water for nitrates. Nitrates in the feed or water plus NPNs in the feed plus

---

* Advanced Biological Concepts, 201 N Railroad Street, Osco, IL 61274-0027; (309) 522-5505; www.abcplus.biz.

excess protein in the total ration can all add up to nitrogen intoxication with a variety of symptoms. One of my clients experienced a devastating storm of abortions within a week after he began feeding some purchased hay that was later found to contain over 5,000 parts per million nitrates.

- Always feed a source of kelp, free choice if possible. Trace mineral–deficient animals will eat a lot until their needs are met. After that, they consume very little. If they continue to eat kelp at high levels, it may indicate a more severe deficiency of one or more individual trace minerals such as zinc, copper, manganese, cobalt, or others. It is possible to self-feed individual sources of these vital trace minerals (usually the chloride or sulfate forms), but great care must be taken to avoid toxicity from overconsumption of improperly made mineral mixes. It is generally safer to buy commercial products as noted above.

- Provide a source of probiotics: lactobacillus, yeast, or other direct-fed microorganisms. A healthy gut is the first line of defense against many bacteria. Probiotics also increase feed efficiency.

Trace Minerals and Free-Choice Mineral Programs

PART 2

5

············

A Brief History of the Free-Choice Concept

As agriculture progressed and animals became domesticated, reports of cattle gnawing on bones (probably for phosphorus), chewing on wood, and eating dirt became common. We were not taught much about animal nutrition in veterinary school in the late 1950s. We were told that if we could recognize the brand name of the feed or mineral being fed, it was probably adequate. Perhaps at that time, over sixty years ago, that dictum was more applicable than it is today. A common mineral mix recommended for livestock use at that time was a third salt, a third finely ground limestone, and a third steamed bonemeal. This was to be provided free choice. The use of salt blocks was common, and there was always some discussion as to the merits of the colored trace mineral blocks over the plain white blocks.

As Linus Pauling, the only person to ever win two unshared Nobel prizes, said "You can trace every disease and every infection to a mineral deficiency from unequally yoked energy fields."

TALBOT-CARLSON, INC.: A PIONEER IN THE INDUSTRY

It is thought that the work of Dr. William Albrecht at the University of Missouri inspired Tully Talbot, a pioneer in animal nutrition. In 1957, using Dr. Albrecht's findings, Tully Talbot started Talbot-Carlson, Inc. (TCI), and developed a free-choice-mineral feeding system for livestock.

His first application was for horses. One instance that illustrates the advantage is an Appaloosa gelding that participated in a two-thousand-mile

endurance race. The horse covered fifty miles per day and never missed a day. He was the only one that achieved this accomplishment in that particular race. This horse was on the free-choice minerals the entire trip, allowing him to adjust his cation/anion ratio and balance his nutritional needs to maintain his workload with different grasses and water every day. This technology was then successfully adapted to beef, dairy, horse, sheep, and goats. After Tully Talbot passed away, the company was dissolved.

A few years later, Bill Johnson, the general manager of the old TCI company, resurrected the concept of individual free-choice minerals and continued to develop and refine the technology under the logo of IDM.

IDM was very successful in introducing this concept to mega-dairies in California. These dairies were fed truck-farm processing waste; for instance, tomato rinds would be fed in the morning and carrot tops in the afternoon. With the free-choice system, the dairies were able to maintain a rolling herd average of seventy to a hundred pounds of milk.

AN INTERESTING HISTORICAL NOTE
FROM BILL JOHNSON

June 8, 2000
To: Advanced Biological Concepts From: Bill Johnson
Subject: Free Choice

During this time of changes in feeding (grazing) and the introduction of new feeds and feeding programs. I would like to remind producers of a tried and proven program that has been used for forty years or more. The idea of free choice is not new; free choice has always been the program of choice by cattle if given the opportunity. Only with fences and confinement were the animals forced to eat what man thought was best for them.

The introduction of free-choice (drug-free) products started in the 1950s by a company in southwest Iowa. Starting with salt, sodium bicarbonate, phosphorus, and calcium, the selection has grown to fourteen or fifteen items available today. Magnesium, trace minerals, and iodine were added in the next couple of years. When I entered the industry in the early seventies the program had grown to ten products, adding potassium, sulfur, and clay with a vitamin A-D-E mix being used mainly in dairy.

The more confined the animal became the harder it was to make this program work. Now people are waking up to the fact that dairy and beef animals do best in a grazing environment and know that grasses change with the seasons and different pastures vary in mineral and energy content.

With free-choice individual minerals (drug-free) the animal can take care of their individual needs (they are all a little different) on a day-to-day basis. This is more economical because you don't force a mix of several minerals to the animal that may only need one or two at the time.

In 1988, Advanced Biological Concepts started manufacturing the product line for IDM. Eventually, Bill Johnson retired and Advanced Biological Concepts purchased IDM, and the company continues to be the premier supplier of individual free-choice minerals and the supporting technology.

While many companies promote free-choice mineral programs, the term with most of these companies refers to making available the one-bag-fits-all conventional mixed minerals, or perhaps two or three different mineral mixes. This is very different from providing a variety of different minerals, cafeteria style, to allow the recipients to self-regulate their individual needs for a dozen or more different minerals.

To my knowledge only three companies focus on individual, free-choice, cafeteria-style mineral programs for livestock:

Advanced Biological Concepts
Jim Helfter
201 N Railroad Street
Osco, IL 61274-0027
1-800-373-5971

Free Choice Enterprises
Mark Bader
10055 County K
Lancaster, WI 53813
608-723-7977

12 Stones Grassland Beef
Bill Roberts
309-714-8789
12StonesGrasslandBeef@gmail.com

6

Tools of the Trade

The other day, when I had my van in the shop for service, I noticed the fine array of wrenches and other tools available for use by the mechanic. Since I am a guy who feels fully equipped if I have more than one adjustable crescent wrench, I was impressed not only by the sheer numbers of the different tools but also by the specific applications for some of them. Given the necessary skills, the mechanic had all the tools he needed to take apart and put back together the complex engines that power today's vehicles.

I remembered then some things I learned years ago from my good friend and veterinary colleague Dr. Bob Scott. Bob had a unique way of looking at things and could translate complicated subjects into easy-to-understand overviews using simple analogies. Below is a summary of his view of the role of minerals in plants and animals.

Plants are basically made up of air and water. If you combine carbon, as from carbon dioxide, with oxygen and hydrogen (from air or water), you have the basic building block for starch, sugar, or carbohydrates. Add nitrogen to this basic formula and you have an amino acid, or a basic building block for protein.

If you burn a plant, thus reducing it to ash, you are left with that part of the plant that came from the soil—usually around 5–10 percent. Therefore, 90–95 percent of the makeup of plants comes from air and water, combined together by the sunshine-generated miracle of photosynthesis.

Minerals are nature's tools that enable this process. They are basic to the enzyme systems that catalyze the storage of the sun's energy into the chemical bonds within the plant itself. The major elements are the big wrenches, and the trace minerals are the smaller ones. All are essential. Any deficiency or imbalance limits the production and the quality of the crops grown. If some elements are lacking in the soil, they will be lacking in the crop. If they are lacking in the crop, they will be lacking in the animal that eats the crop.

When an animal consumes plants, the same tools used by the plant to combine the carbohydrate (CHO) and nitrogen to store energy are needed to break down chemical bonds and release energy to power the metabolic processes of life and production. If the plant does not have enough built-in tools (minerals), extra tools must be provided. Most of our soils are so depleted in minerals that it is almost a given that some sort of mineral supplementation is necessary, especially to arrive at the high levels of productivity that we strive for today. Without the mineral tools, proper digestion and assimilation of the energy in the feeds simply cannot take place.

Even without computers, animals are smarter than man when it comes to balancing their individual needs for the elements of nutrition, especially the major, minor, and trace minerals. Providing a choice in mineral supplementation allows the animals to pick the tools they need without being totally locked-in to only the tools recommended by the computer.

Most farmers probably would not think much of a mechanic that tried to overhaul a tractor with a screwdriver, a pair of pliers, and a couple of crescent wrenches. Unfortunately, in their role as animal caretakers, some livestock men seem to think that a cheap sack of one-bag-fits-all high-calcium minerals and trace mineral salt blocks are all the tools needed by our livestock to fully utilize the energy stored in our feeds. They are wrong!

7

....

A Hundred and
One Nutritionists

A total mixed ration (TMR) is a standard feeding strategy for most large dairies and many small ones. A TMR purports to provide all the nutritional requirements for each cow in the group. A TMR has many advantages for dairymen. Grouping the cows according to common characteristics allows the dairyman or his nutritionist to formulate a daily diet for the average needs of each cow in the group. With a TMR you can quickly and easily reformulate the ration to use different commodities or ingredients as price and availability change. A TMR is easier to feed since everything is rolled up into a neat, one-bag-fits-all package. Dairymen and nutritionists like the precision of a computer printout and the control it gives them over the animal's diet. All of these advantages affect the convenience and control of the managers, but is a TMR really the best way to feed dairy cows?

Remembering that you don't get something for nothing, what is the negative payback for the convenience of using a TMR? Unfortunately, a TMR is a good way to push far more protein than is healthy for ruminants, especially when they do not have the opportunity to adjust their need for fiber in their diet. Bad feet, reproductive problems, and lowered longevity seem to go hand-in-hand with the push for high production at any cost. Perhaps the most meaningful word in the previous paragraph is "average." TMRs are designed to fit the average cow, which means that if a cow does not exactly match the average she will either have certain nutrient excesses or deficiencies to deal with. There is so much individual variation in nutritional needs that it is doubtful we could adjust the TMR to accommodate most of the group. Although some variation is acceptable, in a large group it is theoretically possible that no animal would receive its exact needs. Reducing the size of the group does help, as it tightens up the spread of individual variation. If we carried the "smaller group is better" idea to its extreme we would need a ration for each individual cow, and to go even further over the edge we might need one nutritionist for each cow. How cool would that be? Obviously, that's impracticable, if not impossible, but it does raise an interesting question. What if we could provide a basic feeding strategy that did address the needs of each individual cow for a balance of all nutrients, including carbohydrates, proteins, fats, vitamins, minerals, and water? All animals have the intrinsic ability to balance their nutritional needs if appropriate choices are provided. Here are some steps to build on our nutritional knowledge by taking advantage of animals' nutritional wisdom.

Hey, Doc, Waddaya Got to Care for the Cow and Calf at Calving?

Calving is a critical time for both the cow and the calf. For the two or three weeks immediately prior to freshening and for about the same period afterward, a dairy cow is in a state of increased stress and lower immune function. Problems during this critical time can have adverse effects on health and production that may last throughout the entire lactation. By the same token, anything that you do here to bolster the health and vitality of the cow and calf will certainly benefit the cow during her lactation, and may benefit the calf during its whole life.

We tend to focus on the immediate health and productivity of the cow and her current offspring. We should not overlook the fact that the egg that will produce a calf next year begins its maturation process during this period of immune system suppression. The future health of this calf is greatly affected, for better or for worse, by anything that affects the cow at this critical time. Nutritional balance and mineral balance are extremely important. Providing

---

free-choice individual minerals and trace minerals will help provide this balance.

Allow the cow to calve in a well-bedded, comfortable, private, super-clean maternity pen. Immediately after calving, provide her with ten gallons of warm water with some added electrolytes or salt. This helps her to expel the placenta. Adding fill to the rumen helps to avoid displaced abomasums (the fourth stomach). Remove the placenta as soon as it is expelled. Do not let the cow eat the placenta. This may have been a natural act in the wild to clean up the calving area to avoid predators, but in the modern dairy, a cow eating the placenta may cause digestive problems, lowered peak production, and even death if the undigested membranes lead to a fatal impaction.

Let the cow lick and clean off the calf. Do not let the calf nurse. This interrupts the transfer of disease organisms and parasites to the newborn. Milk out the colostrum and get the calf to take at least a gallon in the first six hours of life. As soon as the calf is dry, remove it to a properly constructed and installed hutch (limited isolation). In a Utah study a few years ago, first-calf heifers raised in a hutch outperformed their group-raised half sisters in the same herd by two thousand pounds of extra milk.

Saturate the navel with iodine as soon as possible after birth. Administer a natural immune stimulant such as colostrum whey immune products.

The gut is the first line of defense against many infections. It has been estimated that 60 percent or more of the immune protective response takes place in the gut. It is important to provide a source of beneficial microorganisms for the first couple of weeks, especially if the dry cow's udder was infused with antibiotics. Antibiotic residues in the milk tend to depress beneficial organisms in the gut.

If possible, feed your best-quality whole milk to your heifer calves.

Everything you do, or don't do, for a calf in the first few hours after birth will have an effect. Do it right and improve herd health now and for future generations.

Originally printed in the June 2008 issue of *The Progressive Dairyman.*

- Use a TMR or a modified TMR to provide basic nutrition. Remember that a cow is a ruminant, so keep the grain-to-roughage ratio as low as possible.
- Provide a separate free-choice source of fiber.
- Provide a free-choice source of individual minerals and trace minerals.
- Feed a high-quality prebiotic/probiotic.

There are several advantages to all this. For one, the animals are healthier and stay in the herd longer. Providing a free-choice source of minerals ensures that each animal has the chance to balance their mineral needs. Trace minerals are the basis for enzymes, which are the spark plugs that enable all metabolic processes. Balance is important—excess can be as damaging as deficiencies. Feeding probiotics increases the digestibility and utilization of all feedstuffs. You get more nutrition from your homegrown feeds and need to buy fewer off-the-farm commodities. This equals more profit.

The bottom line is this: You don't need a hundred and one nutritionists if you allow your cows to be part of your nutritional management team.

8

Mineral Nutrition: Are Animals Nutritionally Wise?

Fred Provenza and Juan J. Villalba

Early studies on nutritional wisdom focused on the innate ability of livestock to balance minerals in their diet. From these studies, nutritionists concluded that livestock are unable to consume minerals in correct quantities to prevent or correct mineral deficiencies and they are not nutritionally wise. However, many of the assumptions nutritionists held about diet selection are questionable if one considers animals must learn about foods and the consequences of eating those foods before they can make correct choices.

Listed below are assumptions implied by nutritional wisdom studies and alternative explanations about how animals learn about foods and nutrients, including minerals.

1. Animals are "genetically programmed" to instinctively recognize needed nutrients similar to the way animals regulate intake of sodium. Animals don't instinctively recognize nutrients. When an animal eats a food that contains needed nutrients, once digested the effects of those nutrients on cells and organ systems in the body feedback to the brain and the animal comes to prefer the food. Thus, experiences with foods shape food preferences.

2. Animals ingest nutrients in exact amounts needed to meet their daily requirements—no under or over consumption. There is no scientific evidence animals eat to prevent nutritional deficiencies. Instead, they respond to excesses, deficits, and imbalances in their diet; the greater the

Excerpted from Fred Provenza and Juan J. Villalba, "Foraging in Domestic Vertebrates: Linking the Internal and External Milieu," ed. V. L. Bels, *Feeding in Domestic Vertebrates: From Structure to Function* (Oxfordshire, UK: CABI Publishing, 2006): 210–40.

excess, deficit, or imbalance, the stronger the response. While they may under- or over-consume needed nutrients within a meal, they generally do a good job of meeting daily nutritional needs. When animals suffer from deficits or imbalances, they seek out different and sometimes unusual foods. If eating a food rectifies the deficiency of imbalance they form a preference for that food.

3. All individuals select nutrients in amounts that match National Research Council (NRC) requirements. Many researchers have little appreciation for individual variation in needs and diet selection. Variation is often viewed as the enemy of statistics. In reality, individuals within a species vary in their need for nutrients. Each animal has its own unique morphology and physiology, which causes it to need and select different amounts of nutrients, including minerals. An animal's experience with foods that provide minerals—bones, urine patches, woodrat houses—also shapes food preferences and influences diet selection.

4. Social learning and culture are not considered in nutritional wisdom. Social learning and culture are critical for animals to acquire nutritional wisdom. Animals that learn about foods from mom or herd mates are more productive than animals that learn about foods by trial and error. Wild animals are often considered better than livestock at balancing their diet. However, wildlife species have an advantage over livestock because they tend to live with their mothers in extended families, facilitating the transfer of information about their environment and foods over a longer period of time. In addition, wildlife tend to live in the same place for generations enabling one generation to pass on information about surviving in their environment to the next.

If animals can learn to prefer foods that contain needed nutrients, then why didn't they learn to consume minerals in the correct amounts when fed in cafeteria trials? Given the design of most mineral cafeteria trials, animals may have been more confused than educated about the value of minerals. Listed below are some possible problems with past studies that may have made it difficult for animals to consume minerals in expected amounts.

1. Sodium was often mixed with every mineral. Many minerals are required in minute amounts so researchers mixed minerals with salt to limit intake. Unfortunately, animals only required a limited amount of sodium each day and it may have either encouraged or limited the intake of other

minerals. Also, given the flavor of sodium, the minerals probably tasted similar. Animals discriminate among foods by flavor. If the minerals tasted similar, animals couldn't associate feedback from the mineral with its flavor.

2. Flavor not color. Researchers colored the minerals so livestock could discriminate among them. As stated above, animals discriminate among foods by flavor—odor plus taste—not color. If foods taste the same, they are the same to the animal regardless of how they look. We select foods the same way. If a bowl of jelly beans are all lime-flavored and you don't like lime jelly beans, then you won't eat them even if they are in different colors. It's flavor that matters.

3. Prevent vs. rectify. Researchers expected animals to eat minerals to prevent deficiencies, but animals eat to correct, not prevent, deficiencies. When animal diets are adequate in nutrients, animals usually continue to eat the same foods. If animals are deficient in nutrients, they seek new foods. Animals develop preference for foods that correct deficiencies.

4. NRC recommendations. Researchers thought animals would eat minerals in the amounts recommended by NRC. However, NRC recommendations are often higher than an animal's needs. Some minerals can be stored in the body and don't need to be consumed each day. In addition, many minerals are only needed in small amounts, a few grams or milligrams per day. A single bite may be more than an animal needs for the day. Finally, whether or not an animal consumes a mineral depends on the mineral status of the animal and the mineral compound offered. For example, cows deficient in calcium tend to avoid phosphorus, thus salts of calcium and phosphorus are poor minerals to use when studying calcium-deficient animals.

LOOKING TO THE FUTURE

Considering the complexities of plants and landscapes, most researchers never imagined that animals were learning about the foods they eat. A better understanding of diet selection is leading to better experiments to determine if animals can learn to rectify mineral deficiencies. One important change in these studies is allowing animals the opportunity to pair the flavor of a mineral with recovery from a deficit of that mineral. These studies show that animals can rectify deficits for energy and protein, and that they balance ratios of energy to protein depending on needs. They also show, in studies done to date, animals rectify deficits for minerals including sodium, calcium, phosphorus, selenium, and sulfur. Most recently, they have been shown to rectify deficits for vitamin E.

Animals have also been shown to make multiple flavor-mineral associations and to select the mineral they are lacking from a choice of minerals. In a recent study, for instance, sheep on a phosphorus (P)-deficient diet increased intake of a P supplement when given a choice between a P, calcium (Ca), or sodium supplement. Conversely, sheep eating a calcium-deficient diet ate more of a Ca supplement than sheep eating a Ca-adequate diet. Calcium-deficient sheep also reduced intake of a P supplement typical of animals on low-calcium diets. In another study, lambs avoided P during periods of P abundance and increased their preference for P during periods of P need. The same has been shown for self-medication for various maladies.

Mineral nutrition is extremely complex. The amount of a particular mineral an animal will ingest depends not only on the level of that mineral in the body but also on its interactions with other minerals in the diet and the body. The body's feedback mechanisms likely enable animals to make correct choices and maintain their mineral status. Recent studies indicate that animals can likely learn to balance minerals in their diets provided they are allowed to pair flavor with recovery from a mineral deficiency.

More information on Dr. Provenza and his research can be found at www.behave.net, which contains a wealth of information including newsletters and fact sheets.

A sixty-three-page booklet written by Dr. Provenza entitled *Foraging Behavior: Managing to Survive in a World of Change* and its companion DVD can be ordered from the Utah State Bookstore in Logan, Utah.*

Selected References

Provenza, F. D. and J. J. Villalba. 2006. Foraging in Domestic Vertebrates: Linking the Internal and External Milieu. Pages 210–240 in V. L. Bels (ed.) *Feeding in Domestic Vertebrates: From Structure to Function.* CABI Publ., Oxfordshire, UK.

Villalba, J. J., F. D. Provenza and J. O. Hall. 2008. Learned appetites for calcium, phosphorus and sodium in sheep. *J. Anim. Sci.* 86:738–747.

---

* Utah State Bookstore, Logan, Utah, 800-662-3950, usubookstore@gmail.com, http:// extension.usu.edu/behave/htm/learning-tools/book-and-dvd.

Villalba, J. J., F. D. Provenza, and R. Shaw. 2006. Sheep self-medicate when challenged with illness-inducing foods. *Anim. Behav.* 71:1131–1139.

Atwood, S.B., F.D. Provenza, R.D. Wiedmeier and R.E. Banner. 2001. Influence of free-choice versus mixed-ration diets on food intake and performance of fattening calves. *J. Anim. Sci.* 79:3034–3040.

Blair-West, J. R., D. A. Denton, M. J. McKinley, B. G. Radden, E. H. Ramshaw, and J. D. Wark. 1992. Behavioral and tissue response to severe phosphorus depletion in cattle. *Am. J. Physiol.* 263:R656–R663.

Coppock, C. E. 1970. Free choice mineral consumption by dairy cattle. Pages 29–35 in *Proc. Cornell Nutr. Conf.*, Ithaca. Cornell Univ. Press, Ithaca, NY.

Coppock, C. E., R. W. Everett, and R. L. Belyea. 1976. Effect of low calcium or low phosphorus diets on free choice consumption of dicalcium phosphate by lactating dairy cows. *J. Dairy Sci.* 59:571–580.

Coppock, C. E., R. W. Everett, and W. G. Merrill. 1972. Effect of ration on free choice consumption of calcium-phosphorus supplements by dairy cattle. *J. Dairy Sci.* 55:245–256.

Denton, D. A., J. R. Blair-West, M. J. McKinley, and J. F. Nelson. 1986. Physiological analysis of bone appetite (osteophagia). *Bioessays* 4:40–42. CrossRefMedline

Launchbaugh, K. L., and F. D. Provenza. 1993. Can plants practice mimicry to avoid grazing by mammalian herbivores? *Oikos* 66:501–504

Leshem, M., S. D. Canho, and J. Schulkin. 1999. Calcium hunger in the parathyroidectomized rat is specific. *Physiol. Behav.* 67:555–559.

McDowell, L. R., and J. D. Arthington. 2005. *Minerals for Grazing Ruminants in Tropical Regions.* 4th ed. University of Florida, IFAS, Gainesville.

Miller, W. J., M. W. Neathery, R. P. Gentry, D. M. Blackmon, C. T. Crowe, G. O. Ware, and A. S. Fielding. 1987. Bioavailability of phosphorus from defluorinated and dicalcium phosphates and phosphorus requirements of calves. *J. Dairy Sci.* 70:1885–1892.

Muller, L. D., L. V. Schaffer, L. C. Ham, and M. J. Owens. 1977. Cafeteria style free-choice mineral feeder for lactating dairy cows. *J. Dairy Sci.* 60:1574–1582.

Pamp, D. E., R. D. Goodrich, and J. C. Meiske. 1977. Free choice minerals for lambs fed calcium- or sulfur-deficient rations. *J. Anim. Sci.* 45:1458–1466. Abstract/FREE Full Text

Provenza, F. D. 1995. Postingestive feedback as an elementary determinant of food preference and intake in ruminants. *J. Range Manage.* 48:2–17. CrossRef

Provenza, F. D. 1996. Acquired aversions as the basis for varied diets of ruminants foraging on rangelands. *J. Anim.* Sci. 74:2010–2020. Abstract/ FREE Full Text

Provenza, F. D., and J. J. Villalba. 2006. Foraging in Domestic Vertebrates: Linking the Internal and External Milieu. Pages 210–240 in *Feeding in Domestic Vertebrates: From Structure to Function.* V. L. Bels, ed. CABI Publ., Wallingford, UK.

Revusky, S. H., M. H. Smith, and D. V. Chalmers. 1971. Flavor preference: Effects of ingestion-contingent intravenous saline or glucose. *Physiol. Behav.* 6:341–343.

Schulkin, J. 1991. *Sodium Hunger: The Search for a Salty Taste.* Cambridge Univ. Press, New York, NY.

Schulkin, J. 2001. *Calcium Hunger. Behavioral and Biological Regulation.* Cambridge Univ. Press, New York, NY.

Tordoff, M. G. 1992. Salt intake of rats fed diets deficient in calcium, iron, magnesium, phosphorus, potassium, or all minerals. *Appetite* 18:29–41.

Tordoff, M. G. 2001. Calcium: Taste, intake, and appetite. *Physiol. Rev.* 81:1567–1597.

Tordoff, M. G. 2002. Intragastric calcium infusions support flavor preference learning by calcium-deprived rats. *Physiol. Behav.* 76:521–529. CrossRefMedline

Underwood, E. J., and N. F. Suttle. 1999. *The Mineral Nutrition of Livestock.* 3rd ed. CABI Publishing, New York, NY.

Villalba, J. J., and F. D. Provenza. 1996. Preference for flavored wheat straw by lambs conditioned with intraruminal administrations of sodium propionate. *J. Anim. Sci.* 74:2362–2368.

Villalba, J. J., and F. D. Provenza. 1997. Preference for flavored wheat straw by lambs conditioned with intraruminal infusions of acetate and propionate. *J. Anim. Sci.* 75:2905–2914.

Villalba, J. J., and F. D. Provenza. 1999. Nutrient-specific preferences by lambs conditioned with intraruminal infusions of starch, casein, and water. *J. Anim. Sci.* 77:378–387.

9

....

Research Efforts Have Lagged in Free-Choice Feeding

George T. Barrows

It appears that many knowledgeable scientists and researchers in a number of fields agree that animals have an amazing ability to self-select ration components. Logically, the question arises in every paper, whether it is possible to supply these ration components separately in a manner that the animal can recognize and consume.

In order to survive, animals not only have to find a sufficient quantity of food, but they must also obtain nutritionally adequate substances. Animals must, therefore, exhibit some degree of selection in their ingestion of feedstuffs.

To survive and therefore reproduce, animals historically have been required to associate foods with the consequences of their ingestion. To ignore this fact leaves us with the unfeasible alternative that all food getting is entirely haphazard or entirely determined by genetics.

A great number of experiments and field trials have documented the ability of animals to select and qualitatively monitor their intake of nutrients. These studies are from a number of fields including nutrition, physiology, genetics, agriculture, psychology, medicine, and veterinary medicine.

The research in this area has at times been both confusing and contradictory. In most cases, animals have either been placed on a total self-selection regimen or have been allowed a limited choice of a small number of mixed diets or nutrient solutions. Under total self-selection, the animal is offered an array of either purified or natural feedstuffs and allowed to choose its

Reprinted from *Animal Nutrition & Health*, May 1977.

diet completely. The alternative methods usually involve a two-choice situation between more or less nutritionally adequate diets or the provision on one diet and the choice of several solutions. Often, the total self-selection method has been used in the absence of any manipulation simply to test the selection ability and nutrient requirements of normal animals. The two most common methods of inducing a need have been through the feeding of a deficient diet and through physiological intervention by surgical procedures or drug injections.

ANIMAL STUDIES

Work done with rats indicates a positive ability of the animal to self-select its diet. Curt Richter has done extensive investigation into the self-regulatory behavior of animals. In one case, he offered female rats casein, sucrose, yeast, olive oil, and six vitamins and mineral solutions. All animals survived and, despite a 20 percent lower caloric intake, showed weight gains equivalent to a control group placed on stock laboratory diet.[1] Griffith and Alexander report satisfactory selection and normal fat intake with Norway rats.[2] In another of the few experimental selection studies that have used a non-domesticated species, Harriman found that seven plains woodrats successfully selected a balanced diet from a choice of casein, sucrose, vegetable oil, and a mineral mix.[3]

In other studies, Davis maintained children up to four and a quarter years on a self-selected regimen. At no time during this period was any effort made to control the children's intake of the thirty unseasoned and unmixed foods that were used. All children were judged to be exceptionally healthy and were largely or entirely free from digestive upsets such as diarrhea, constipation, or stomach upset. In addition, one child admitted to the program with an advanced stage of rickets showed a marked appetite for cod liver oil. This appetite disappeared when the ricketic symptoms were no longer demonstrable on X-rays.[4]

Albrecht noted that cows allowed to graze from four haystacks ate exclusive from the single stack made of hay grown on fertilized soil. A chemical analysis revealed that the hay chosen was slightly, though consistently, of better nutritive quality.[5]

Green found that in the phosphorus-poor grazing land of South Africa, cattle frequently became osteophagic, or bone eaters, presumably to satisfy their phosphorus requirements. The addition of phosphorus to the ration caused a cessation of the bone-eating pica.[6] Gordon, Tribe, and Graham pastured a sheep on a phosphorus-poor grazing area, but found neither pica nor an appetite for phosphorus salts despite decreased levels of blood phosphorus.[7] McCandish, Nevens, and Evvard demonstrated that cows, on total self-selection maintenance with a number of feeds such as grain, oatmeal, and roughages have shown selection abilities that allow normal to above normal growth and production.

The same authors conducted a similar study with swine and observe a favorable growth rate. One sow grew to be the largest pig producer at the Iowa Agricultural Station up to that time.[8,9,10] Glimp noted that as sheep mature they select a diet of increasing protein and energy content.[11] A number of self-selection studies with chickens have been conducted which have been successful, relative to control.[12]

VITAMIN SELECTION

Richter was the first to show animals' apparent recognition of dietary vitamins. He and his coworkers implicated a role of the B vitamin in protein and carbohydrate metabolism and also a possible B vitamin sparing action fat. They found when rats were made nitrogen deficient, their protein and carbohydrate intakes decreased while their fat intakes showed a marked increase. Richter also demonstrated the ability of animals to select not only the B-complex vitamins but also A, D, and E.[13,14,15] Many authors have studied the effects of physiological manipulation on dietary free choicing. For example, following the removal of the parathyroids, which results in excess calcium excretion and phosphorus rejection, Richter and Echert found in rats a decreased phosphorus intake and an increased ingestion of calcium, strontium, and magnesium solutions. These self-selecting animals were able to keep themselves free of tetany, a diagnostic symptom of calcium deficiency.[16]

An interesting study on the role of self-selection is by Emmers and Nocenti. Parathyroidectomized rats were placed on a total self-selection, and the characteristic increase in calcium intake was observed. Half the animals then underwent an ablation of the thalamic gustatory nucleus. The ablation of the nucleus was complete, and there was a failure of calcium selection resulting in tetany and death.[17]

Overmann describes an experimental method of total self-selection of nutrients by animals allowed to regulate their ingestion of a wide variety of feedstuffs which are either isolated nutrients of naturally occurring but incomplete feeds. With limited choice of selection, however, the animals were given two or more essentially nutritionally complete diets for a single diet and a choice of solutions.

A common practice in these studies is to induce a dietary need through the feeding of a deficient diet or one enriched in the needed nutrient. A specific hunger or satisfactory selection is demonstrated if the deficient animals show a preference for the enriched feed or if enough of the enriched diet is ingested to alleviate deficiency symptoms.

The nutrients which have received the largest amount of experimental attention with this method are the B vitamins, especially thiamine.[18] Harris, Clay, Hargreaves, and Ward demonstrated that vitamin B–deficient rats were shown to prefer a diet enriched with a natural, distinctively flavored vitamin D supplement over a deficient diet lacking the supplement. The rats were also able to discriminate between diets containing different percentages of the natural supplements.[19]

Chesyers and Quarterman, 1970, and Christensen, Caldwell, and Oberlas, 1974, demonstrated that zinc-deficient rats have shown an increased intake of zinc-containing solutions or diets.[20, 21] In 1914, Evvard tried a free-choice system of feeding pigs and concluded that the appetite of the pig appears to be a very good guide as to its body needs.[10]

F. R. Bell demonstrated a precise taste threshold for ruminants associated with sodium depletion. He concluded his paper by saying, "It becomes apparent, therefore, that in ruminants there is a close interrelationship between taste, metabolism, and nutrition." At present, the experimental data is sparse, but the availability of good experiment preparations augurs well for future investigation.[22]

MINERAL PREFERENCE

The Kerr Foundation, in its 1969 Nine-Year Research report, discusses a three-year experiment evaluating the ability of cattle to select major and trace minerals free choice. The minerals offered were potassium, phosphorus, sodium, sulfur, magnesium, calcium, and sodium chloride. The minor minerals offered were iron, manganese, zinc, boron, copper, cobalt, iodine, and a control. Their conclusions were: "To determine the results of this experiment, it appears to be necessary to break the minerals into major and minor elements. This appears to be especially important in trying to deter-

Ohio Study on Mineral Consumption in Horses: Calcium-Phosphorus Balance

According to an article in *Horse Care Review*,* W. J. Tyznik, a nutritionist formerly on staff at Ohio State University, reported on experiments regarding the calcium- and phosphorus-regulating ability of horses. In his experiments, four boxes containing plain salt, trace mineral salt, pulverized limestone, and a phosphorus supplement were placed in widely separated locations in test horses' stalls. To prove the horses' regulating ability with these minerals, Tyznik had the location of each box changed and the amount of each supplement weighed weekly. The weights noted each week were compared with those of the previous week to determine the amount of each supplement consumed that week.

Tyznik discovered that by changing from high-calcium to low-calcium natural feeds, the horses would seek out the correct boxes and adjust their calcium and phosphorus consumption according to the ration, and at all times they maintained the proper amounts of calcium and phosphorus in the body tissues and circulating blood.

---

* "In Search of Horse Nutrition," *Horse Care Review* 1, no. 2 (Fall 1976), quoted in George T. Barrows, "Research Efforts Have Lagged in Free-Choice Feeding," *Animal Nutrition and Health* (May 1977).

mine if cattle can select these elements. Salt consumption appears to be consumed in relation to the sodium and chloride content of the grass.

"Calcium is another element where it appears that consumption is related to the content of the grass. Phosphorus and magnesium were also consumed in amounts that closely followed the grass analysis. The trace minerals appeared to have delayed reaction to the element in the grass. Consumption of all the elements tended to decline as the cows increased in age. Primary consumption of the minor minerals including salt occurred in October, November, December, January, February, and March: and primary consumption of the minor minerals occurred during March, April, May, June."[23]

Richter concluded, "Proof of the existence of behavior regulators was taken from experiments in the field of endocrinology and nutrition. It was shown that disturbances created in the internal environment by removal of one of the other of the endocrine glands were corrected by the animals themselves. It was demonstrated that the ability to select diets with relation to internal needs seems to depend more on taste sensations than on experience, and it was pointed out that this knowledge of the ability of animals to make beneficial selections can be used to study a variety of the problems in the field of endocrinology and nutrition.

"Evidence was further presented for the existence and successful operation of similar behavior regulators in human beings. Thus, we believe that the results of our experiments indicate that in human beings and animals the effort to maintain a constant internal environment or homeostasis constitutes one of the most universal and purposeful of all behavior urges or drives."[24]

STUDY COMPARISON DIFFICULT

Other scientists have completed work that agrees with Richter. For example, Overmann concludes, "Animals do exhibit the ability to select and regulate their ingestion of nutrients. This ability has been demonstrated in a number of species under a variety of conditions and with a host of different nutrient sources. Although the diversity of methods, animals and feedstuffs adds substantial evidence to the validity of dietary self-selection abilities, it has also contributed to an apparent lack of reliability. Comparisons between studies are difficult and contradictory findings are common."[18]

Rozin has pointed out, however, that positive demonstrations of selection or regulation must be considered more convincing than negative findings, lack of selection or regulation.[25] One primary factor contributing to these contradictions between studies is the nutrients offered to animals. Various feedstuffs differ widely in palatability and nutritional value.

Selected References

1. Richter CP. "Total Self-Regulator Functions in Animals and Human Beings." Harvey Lecture Series, 1943, 38, 63–103.
2. Griffith, PR, and Alexander, JC. "Effect of Zinc Deficiency on Amino Acid Metabolism of the Rat." *Nutrition Reports International*, 1972, vol. 6, 9–20.

3. Harriman, AE. "Self-Selection of Diet by Southern Plains Wood Rats (*Neotoma micropus*)." *Journal of General Psychology*. 90(1): 53–61.

4. Davis, C. "Studies in the Self-Selection of Diet by Young Children." *Journal of the American Dental Association*, 1974, 193–94, 21, 636–40.

5. Albrecht, W. "The Story of the Four Haystacks." *The Land*, 1945, 4, 228–32.

6. Green, H. "Perverted Appetites." *Physiological Review*, 1925, 5, 336–48.

7. Gordon, J, Tribe, D, and Graham, R. "The Feeding Behavior of Phosphorus Deficient Cattle and Sheep." *British Journal of Animal Behavior*, 1954.

8. McCandlish, A. "Studies in the Growth and Nutrition of Dairy Calves. VII The Use of the Self-Feeder with Young Dairy Calves." *Journal of Dairy Science*, 1923, 6, 500–502.

9. Nevens, W. "Experiments in the Self-Feeding of Dairy Cows." *Illinois Agricultural Experiment Station Bulletin*, 1927, no. 289.

10. Edward, J. "Is the Appetite of Seine a Reliable Indication of Physiological Need?" *Proceedings of the Iowa Academy of Science*, 1915, 22, 375–402.

11. Glimp, H. "Effect of Diet Composition on Diet Preference by Lambs." *Journal of Animal Science*, 1971, 33, 861–64.

12. Tomhave, C, and Barelare, B. "Self-Selection of Feeds by Hens." *Delaware Agricultural Station Bulletin*, 1931, no. 174.

13. Richter, C, Hold, L, and Barelare, B. "The Effect of Self-Selection of Diet-Food (Protein, Carbohydrates, and Fats) Minerals and Vitamins on Growth, Activity and Reproduction of Rats." *American Journal of Physiology*, 1937, 119, 383–89.

14. Richter, C, Hold, L, and Barelare, B. "Vitamin B Craving in Rats." *Science*, 1937, 86, 354–55.

15. Richter, C, Hold, L, Barelare, B, and Hawkes, C. "Changes in Fat, Carbohydrate and Protein Appetite in Vitamin B Deficiency." *American Journal of Physiology*, 1938, 124, 596, 602.

16. Richter, C, and Eckert, J. "Mineral Appetite of Parathyroidectomized Rats." *American Journal of Medical Science*, 1939, 198, 9–16.

17. Emmers, R, and Nocenti, M. "Role of Thalamic Gustatory Nucleus in Diet Selection by Norman and Parathyroidectomized Rats." *Proceed-*

ings of the Society for Experimental Biology and Medicine, 1967, 125, 1264–70.

18. Overmann, S, and Yang, M. "Adaptation to Water Restriction through Dietary Selection in Weaning Rats." *Physiology and Behavior*, 1973, 11, 781–86.

19. Harris, L, Clay, J, Hargreaves, F, and Ward, A. "Appetite and Choice of Diet. The Ability of Vitamin B Deficient Rats to Discriminate between Diets Containing and Lacking the Vitamin." *Proceedings of the Royal Society (Section B)*, 1933, 113, 161–90.

20. Chesters, J, and Quarterman, J. "Effects of Zinc Deficiency on Food Intake and Feeding Pattern of Rats." *British Journal of Nutrition*, 1970, 24, 1061–69.

21. Christensen, C, Caldwell, D, and Oberleas, D. "Establishment of a Learned Preference for a Zinc-Containing Solution by Zinc-Deficient Rats." *Journal of Comparative and Physiological Psychology*, 1974, 87, 415–31.

22. Bell, FR. "The Variation in Taste Thresholds of Ruminant Associated with Sodium Depletion." *Journal of Comparative and Physiological Psychology*. In: Zotterman Y, editor. *Olfaction and taste I*. Oxford: Pergamon Press; 1963, 299–307.

23. Wilson, B, and Cupp, W. *Project 1-1: An Evaluation of the Ability of Cattle to Select Major and Trace Minerals Free Choice* (unpublished).

24. Richter, C. "Total Self Regulatory Functions in Animals and Human Beings." Harvey Lecture Series, 1943, 38, 63–103.

25. Rozin, P. "Are Carbohydrates and Protein Intakes Separately Regulated?" *Journal of Comparative Physiological Psychology*, 1968, 65, 23–29.

26. Albrecht, W. "Livestock Can Teach Us a Lesson from the Ground Up." *Breeder Gazette*, April 1964.

27. Kuck, ER. "How Guernsey Calves Helped Solve a Feed and Crop Fertilization Problem." *Better Crops*, December 1946.

28. Anonymous, "In search of Horse Nutrition." *Horse Care Review*. Fall 1976 vol. 1, no. 2.

29. Church, DC, et al. *Digestive Physiology and Nutrition of Ruminants*, vol. 2. Corvallis, Oregon: D. C. Church, 1971, 406, 408.

10

Research: Reading between the Lines

I have been involved with the concept of self-feeding individual minerals for over fifty years: as a veterinarian, as a livestock owner, and as an industry consultant. In my experience it works most of the time—but not always. When it does not seem to work, it's common to find water problems or gross nutritional imbalances of protein, carbohydrates, and fiber.

Unfortunately there is a paucity of meaningful university research on either side of this issue, and much of it is outdated because of the many changes in livestock management that have taken place over the years. Then, too, most of the early research fell into the trap of trying to reduce a highly complex biological phenomenon to a single-factor analysis of the consumption patterns of just a few minerals over a short time period. Also, unfortunately, much of our research is designed to prove a theory or provide the basis for a sales pitch and not to investigate what is actually happening.

We rely a lot on university research in many of our management decisions. Oftentimes this is useful, and sometimes not. To critically evaluate research there are several things you should take into account.
- Who paid for the research?
- Who did the research?
- Where did the researcher work before?
- Where does the researcher anticipate working in the future?
- Has the researcher ever served on boards of commercial companies in related industries?

- Has the researcher ever worked for government agencies that regulate any aspect of the agricultural industry?
- Have you examined the whole content of the research in the light of common sense?

Keeping these cautions in mind, remember many researchers are right on point. Consider this statement from Dr. R. L. Preston, PhD, professor emeritus from Texas Tech University in Lubbock, Texas:

> Feeds can be chemically analyzed for many things which may or may not be related to the response of an animal when fed the feed. The response of cattle and sheep when fed a feed, however, can be termed the biological response to the feed in question, which is a function of its chemical composition and the ability of the animal to derive useful nutrient value from the feed. The latter relates to the digestibility or availability of a nutrient in the feed for absorption into the body and its ultimate efficiency of use in the animal, depending on the nutrient status of the animal and the productive or physiological function being performed by the animal. Thus, ground fence posts and shelled corn may have the same gross energy value in a bomb calorimeter, but have markedly different useful energy value (TDN, digestible energy, net energy) when consumed by the animal. That means that the biological attributes of a feed have much greater meaning in predicting the productive response of animals, but are much more difficult to accurately determine because there is an interaction between the chemical composition of the feed with the digestive and metabolic capabilities of the animal being fed.

Unfortunately, often the conclusions or summary statements in a research report do not match the actual data or results. Here is an example of erroneous conclusion drawn by some researchers.

In 1977 a study was done at South Dakota State University entitled "Cafeteria Style Free-Choice Mineral Feeder for Lactating Dairy Cows."*

---

* L. D. Muller, L. V. Schaffer, L. C. Ham, and M. J. Owens, "Cafeteria Style Free-Choice Mineral Feeder for Lactation Dairy Cattle," South Dakota State University, Dairy Science Department, *Journal of Dairy Science* 60, no. 10 (May 1977): 1574–82.

The authors stated, "Little evidence was found that dairy cows offered minerals and vitamins free choice consumed to a specific appetite or need under the two nutritional regimes."

Let's take a closer look of some of the excerpts from that study, along with some of my comments in italics.

"Trial 1 was 16 weeks in which two groups of cows in mid-lactation (10 cows / group) were group-fed rations with either corn silage or alfalfa hay as the sole forage, and all supplemental minerals and vitamins were provided free choice." *This is too small a group and too short a time to really evaluate the nutritional wisdom of animals. A full twelve months would be better as that would encompass the gamut of lactation, dry period, parturition, and back to lactation. Even better would be a multiyear experiment that examines*

Chart 10.1: Free-Choice Intake of Minerals and Vitamins from Cafeteria Mineral Feeder (Trial 1)

Item	Silage		Alfalfa	
		(g/cow/day)		
Bentonite	78.3	(2–169)[a]	82.3	(30–134)[a]
Calcium	9.8	(0–84)	7.8	(0–66)
Iodine	0.05	(0–0.35)	0.01	(0–0.09)
Magnesium	2.6	(0–7.3)	1.9	(0.3–5.0)
Phosphorus	8.3[b]	(2.1–15.9)	16.3[c]	(9.0–24.4)
Potassium	14.6[b]	(1.5–28.7)	0.4[c]	(0–2.3)
Salt	8.4	(0–19.5)	5.2	(013.2)
Bicarbonate	6.6	(0–17.7)	6.9	(0–16.9)
Sulfur	2.4	(0.8–7.5)	1.5	(0–2.9)
Trace minerals	1.9	(0–8.9)	1.9	(0–5.0)
		(IU/cow/day)		
Vitamin A	134,600[b]	(0–450,000)	72,916[c]	(7,600–258,000)
Vitamin D	67,348[b]	(0–225,000)	36,458[c]	(3,800–129,000)
Vitamin E	34[b]	(0–62)	18[c]	(2–64)

[a] Values in parentheses are daily intake ranges per cow based on weekly measurements.
[b,c] Means in same row differ (P<0.01).

Source: L. D. Muller, L. V. Schaffer, L. C. Ham, and M. J. Owens, "Cafeteria Style Free-Choice Mineral Feeder for Lactation Dairy Cattle," South Dakota State University, Dairy Science Department, *Journal of Dairy Science* 60, no. 10 (May 1977): 1574–82.

the health and productivity of the calves born to the two research groups, thus evaluating the multigenerational effect.

"Minerals and vitamins were provided in a 'cafeteria style' mineral feeder, one feeder per group. The feeder was sheltered and afforded protection from wind and rain. Mineral and vitamin mixes were: calcium (28 to 30% Ca from calcium carbonate), phosphorus (>20% P from monosodium phosphate), potassium (>31% K from potassium chloride), magnesium (21.5% Mg from magnesium oxide and sulfate), sulfur (47.5% S from flours of sulfur), trace mineral, bicarbonate of soda, sodium bentonite, sodium chloride, iodine mix (>.88% I), and vitamins A, D, and E (Vitamin A, 4,400,000 U.S.P. units/kg; Vitamin D, 2,200,000 U.S.P. units/kg; and Vitamin E, 1,100 IU/kg). The remaining portions of the mineral mixes were composed of products such as rice mill by-products, rice hulls, and dehydrated alfalfa. Intake of each individual mineral was determined weekly for each group.

"Intake of phosphorus, potassium, and vitamins differed between rations. A higher free choice intake of phosphorus by cows fed alfalfa was not expected." *It should have been expected as it is well-known that cattle need to balance their Ca:P ratio.* "Cows could possibly have been consuming more P to narrow the wide Ca:P ratio due to high Ca intake from alfalfa." *Of course they ate more phosphorus to balance the high calcium in alfalfa. That's what free-choice is all about—giving them the opportunity to self-regulate their needs.*

"Cows fed corn silage consumed more potassium free-choice, but additional intake still was needed to meet requirements." *Whose requirements are they trying to meet—National Research Council (NRC) standards or what the cow actually needs? The authors could not explain why this group's milk production exceeded the alfalfa group even with their assumed potassium deficiency.*

"Little evidence was found in these two short trials that lactating dairy cows have a specific appetite for individual minerals. Where corn silage and alfalfa, forages that differ in mineral content, were fed as the sole forages to two groups of cows, only in the cases of potassium and vitamins did cows fed corn silage consume large amounts free-choice possibly to compensate for a dietary deficiency." *Actually the main mineral ratios were balanced by the cow's mineral preferences. They balanced the critical Ca:P ration by eating more phosphorus to compensate for the high calcium in alfalfa. The cows in the alfalfa* group took almost no potassium while the corn silage group consumed thirty-six times more potassium than the alfalfa group.

Given the above perspective, it's difficult to understand how the authors concluded that cattle cannot balance their own mineral needs.

11

Design Considerations for a Self-Regulated Mineral Program

When choosing a free-choice mineral program, there are a few things you should keep in mind. A cafeteria-style, self-regulated mineral program must be designed to allow the animal to use its natural, instinctive, selective ability to satisfy nutrient requirements with specific references to minerals and vitamins. Contrary to what some seem to think, selective breeding has not reduced animals' abilities to choose those nutrients necessary to their well-being any more than selective breeding has reduced the sex drive or the animal's need to consume nutrients for energy or protein. Animals will select needed minerals and vitamins in proportion to palatability (solubility) of the individual compounds used in the formulation of the various mineral products. Thus, formulators must use quality products that will be soluble in the animal's mouth so that the taste bud system, which is triggered by deficiencies of nutrients in the tissue of the animal and more specifically the blood, will recognize the nutrients by its own merits. Flavoring agents added to entice the animal to consume minerals must not be used.

The major benefit of a cafeteria-style mineral program is that it not only allows the animal to satisfy mineral deficiencies of the present ration, but it also allows the animal to consume additional minerals as necessary to satisfy tissue deficiencies caused by previous unbalanced rations. This results in the consumption, at times, of minerals in amounts some would consider beyond the needs of a given ration.

When offering nutrients on a separate and free-choice basis, husbandry men must clearly understand that animals will satisfy total nutrient needs. Consequently, the animal may need to consume additional amounts of the particular mineral in question until its tissue deficiencies are adequately satisfied. At that time the animal will consume only the amounts of the individual minerals necessary to satisfy deficiencies of the present ration, with little or no consideration for the previous history of deficiencies. Scientific research has proven time and again that various mineral deficiencies within the physiological system of the animal prevent it from producing and or reproducing at optimum. A cafeteria-style mineral program allows the animal to satisfy these physiological needs and satisfy deficiencies of the present ration.

MINERAL ELEMENT RELATIONSHIPS

Before beginning a free-choice mineral program, you must be very aware of the interrelationship of the tremendous number of mineral elements. Many feedstuffs contain excesses of mineral elements that some seem to consider of no consequence. Nothing could be further from the truth. If we consider simply the Ca:P ratio, then a ration that contains 1 percent calcium will cause the animal to consume quantities of phosphorus in amounts that may seem excessive. But if we consider that the animal's physiological system functions best with a proper ratio, then it becomes logical that the animal will consume amounts of phosphorus necessary to attempt to provide its system with that ratio. Genetic selection has created animals with different mineral needs than those currently published in nutrition requirement charts. A self-regulated mineral program provides a more accurate mineral balance to range animals in the multitude of various soil types, climatic conditions, and animal genetics.

Healthy animals are animals that are more productive. Even in the present economic circumstances, a self-regulated mineral program is economical:

1. By supplying the necessary mineral element to better balance the ration so that it can be digested more efficiently
2. By allowing the animal to be in better physiological condition so that it will be more productive and or reproductive
3. By not forcing unnecessary and unneeded minerals into any animal

Hey, Doc, Waddaya Got for the Newborn Calf?

Over time, I have become more appreciative of the influence of those great teachers from whom we have learned professional skills and correct principles. One such person for me was Dr. Wesley Crenshaw, an anatomy professor at the University of Missouri Veterinary School.

Crenshaw was my pre-vet student adviser as well as the instructor of histology (microscopic anatomy) for first-year vet students. As we peered through the microscope at seemingly countless tissue slides, the good doctor would constantly remind us, "You have to know the normal to be able to recognize the abnormal." With that principle in mind, let's consider the "normal" calving phenomenon as it occurred prior to domestication, or as close as we can come to that happy state in today's modern world.

I have always been fascinated to observe how domestic animals act when left without much human intervention. Our weekly drive to church on Sunday mornings takes us by a hillside pasture where a cattleman calves out his Angus cows in the spring. The lay of the land gives an unobstructed view of the entire pasture. Since the cow's natural inclination is to seek out a private, secluded place in which to deliver her calf, we observe that each cow-calf pair will evenly distance themselves from the others and will maintain this isolation for several days. After a few weeks, it's common to see calves gathered together in small groups of five or six and guarded by a lone sentinel cow. I often wonder how this "babysitter" cow is chosen, or if each mother cow takes her turn on a rotational basis. As more calves are born, other groups are eventually formed, and these groups gradually intermingle until the calves become fully integrated into the herd.

There are two main advantages of this naturally occurring limited isolation. In conjunction with the protective effects of colostrum, this seclusion gives the calf's immature immune system time to develop by having a successful response to its first mild exposure. It also minimizes exposure of the whole group in case one calf becomes sick. Whether you are raising beef calves or dairy calves, remember that adequate colostrum as an immune support and limited isolation for the newborn are the pillars of nature's plan to ensure healthy calves.

Our modern methods of raising dairy calves have come a long way from a natural environment. It is a tribute to the calf's versatility that she is able to adapt as well as she does to these changes. The essence of holistic calf management is to combine the best of our modern technology with natural principles to develop a program that encourages the calf to reach its highest level of health and productivity. To the extent that we can mimic nature, we will be more successful and have fewer problems.

The one thing absolutely necessary to delivering and raising a healthy calf is to have a healthy mother cow. At birth, a newborn calf will only be as healthy as its dam. If a mother cow suffers from malnutrition, immune suppression, and subclinical infections, it will affect the health of the calf and its susceptibility to disease organisms encountered early in life.

If a calf suffers from a severe case of scours and pneumonia (they frequently go together), the health and productivity of that animal will probably be impaired for the rest of its life due to damaged tissue in the gut or lungs. Prevention is thus much more important than treating problems after the damage is done.

Following are some items to be considered when formulating your prevention strategy.

- Make sure the cow is in good health and your vaccination program (if you have one) is up-to-date.
- Provide a sanitary maternity pen or area for the cow to calve in.
- At calving let the cow lick and clean off the calf. Do not let the calf nurse. This interrupts the transfer of disease organisms (especially Johne's) and parasites to the newborn. Milk out the colostrum and get the calf to take at least a gallon in the first six hours of life. If the cow was added to the herd less than three weeks before calving, her colostrum immunoglobulins may not be specific to the calf's birth environment. In that case, supple-

mental colostrum from other cows in the herd may be advantageous.

- Milk replacers, if used, should be milk-based and not based on soybean meal. It's best to use the dam's milk or milk from the parent herd. Do not feed throwaway, mastitic milk. If you must feed discarded milk, pasteurize it before feeding.
- The gut is the first line of defense against many infections. As soon as possible, give the calf a source of beneficial lactobacillus or other prebiotics and probiotics.
- As soon as possible after birth, administer any immune stimulants you have available, such as colostrum whey products, homeopathic remedies, herbs, etc.
- Saturate the navel with a strong iodine solution as soon as possible after birth.
- When the calf is dry, move it to a properly constructed and installed calf hutch. Leave it in the hutch for six to eight weeks or until weaned. Applying this natural concept of "limited isolation" is an excellent way to avoid most health problems in the neonate.

Even under the best of circumstances, problems will occur. When confronted with a case of scours, it is helpful to have a rough diagnosis of the cause.

If the scours are nutritional in origin, the calf usually has a normal temperature with white or yellow feces. Adjusting the amount and/or temperature of the milk fed along with adding some probiotics will usually remedy that situation. The core body temperature is about 38.5°C or 101°F. I would become alarmed if the temperature was more than one and a half to two degrees on either side of this. If the calf does have a fever and the feces are watery, foul smelling, and yellowish-brown in color or contain blood or mucus, the scours is almost always infectious in nature. The age of the calf at onset may also give some clues as to the specific cause. E. coli scours is common in calves from one to three day old. At five to fifteen days of age, rotavirus and coronavirus should be suspected. Salmonella may occur from two to six weeks of age.

The toxins produced by E. coli and other infections cause increased secretion of fluid and electrolytes into the intestines with the resulting diarrhea and dehydration. Regardless of the cause of the problem or of the treatment options, you must address the dehydration first. You can evaluate the degree of dehydration by simply pinching and pulling up a fold of skin on the neck or shoulder, "tenting" the skin. In a normal calf the skin snaps back almost immediately. If dehydration is present, the skin stays tented for a longer time. The longer it takes for the skin to return to normal, the higher the degree of dehydration. In severe dehydration, the eyeballs sink away from the eyelids. This is sure sign that oral electrolytes are needed immediately. Oral electrolytes are used to correct the imbalances in the calf's system by restoring lost fluids, electrolyte balance, glucose levels, and acid/base ratios.

There are many brands of electrolytes available, and many are prohibitively overpriced. Here is a recipe for a homemade oral electrolyte that can be used routinely or in an emergency.

Add to 1 gallon of water:
- 86 grams (3 ounces) of table sugar or dextrose/glucose (corn syrup)
- 14 grams (0.5 ounces) of baking soda (bicarb)
- 13 grams (0.5 ounces) of table salt
- 3 grams (0.1 ounces) of potassium chloride (use if available; if not, don't worry—it's not critical

You can feed a quart or two of this mixture three to four times a day. Stagger it with the milk feeding, leaving at least a two-hour interval between the milk and electrolyte feedings.

Along with restoring the electrolyte balance, it's important to continue to meet the calf's nutritional needs. Even though a case of scours may damage some of the intestinal lining, other segments are still able to absorb nutrients from milk. Baby calves don't have large reserves of glycogen and fat to meet their energy needs when they are not being fed milk. Thus, it is critical that scouring calves continue to receive adequate milk. Sometimes it may be advisable to slightly reduce the quantity of milk fed for a short time, but never completely withhold milk for more than twenty-four hours. If calves are too weak to eat, you may need to use an esophageal feeder to administer their milk feedings.

Concurrent with the above treatment, it is also necessary to address the cause of the problem with the appropriate medical therapy. This is the time to invoke the healing properties of your favorite herbs, homeopathic preparations, colostrum products, acupuncture, or other products or management practices to boost immunity and help the patient throw off the disease-causing infection. These treatments are mostly effective, especially when used with hydration and nutrition management as described above.

Everything you do, or don't do, for a calf in the first few hours or days after birth will have an effect. Do it right and improve herd health now and in the future.

I learned most of these concepts and practices from my association over the years with good dairymen who have years of field experience to draw on. I believe that good animal husbandry principles learned by astute dairymen observing nature over a period of time are just as accurate and meaningful as university research. There is little academic support for some of these ideas since they do not attract much research funding. The upside is that they cost little or nothing to try, they have no side effects, and if they don't work for you at least you have done no harm.

4. By allowing the animal to adjust its mineral intake to maintain a balanced diet as ration quality changes, due to either changing feedstuffs or climatic conditions
5. By allowing individual animals to selectively satisfy individual needs, which is not possible with a mixed or force-fed mineral program

The end results in improved health, which allows the animal to better produce to its genetic potential.

ALL MINERALS ARE NOT THE SAME

Consider the following facts. Feed tags do not tell the whole story. Two mineral tags may show the same ingredient list and guaranteed analysis yet still vary greatly in cost and in nutritional performance. You get what you pay for: cheap minerals are often the most expensive in the long run! If you make the wrong choice you are actually setting a timer for production and reproduction failure.

A top-of-the-line mineral will contain broad-spectrum prebiotic, probiotic, and enzymatic products that enable your animals to efficiently digest fiber and protein in the ration and thus release the minerals and other nutritional ingredients already present in your feed for greater cost savings. Fiber digestion provides a source of major and microminerals in a natural, chelated form.

Cheap sources of some minerals are not as readily available to the recipient animal. They then have to consume more to satisfy their nutritional needs. Excess consumption can result in mineral imbalances that lower immune response and productivity

Properly formulated minerals do not contain consumption limiters to limit consumption of the more expensive items. This is false economy as it does not allow the animals to take what they need to maintain health. Make sure the minerals do not contain enhancers to force consumption of some items so that they conform to university standards for mineral consumption. This practice forces the animals to consume an unbalanced mineral diet and also sets the timer for future problems.

Cheap sources of minerals are more likely to be contaminated with toxic heavy metals. More and more minerals (less expensive but of poorer quality) are being imported from foreign countries. Phosphorus and zinc sources imported from China have been found contaminated with cadmium and have been determined to be responsible for toxic symptoms in some herds.

Whenever you buy minerals, it is best to know your suppliers and buy from a company that has a history of success.

12

Troubleshooting a Mineral Program

Although most mineral feeding programs are fairly easy to use, it's not uncommon to have a few questions or difficulties when first starting out. In this chapter, I will walk you through some common issues that may arise when you begin implementing a free-choice mineral program. The Helfter Feeds Mineral Program, for example, will work, as designed, to provide profits to the customer. The five-point feeding program is a vital part of the program. Violation of this five-point program, to any degree, may be expected to cause a decrease in efficiency of production, reproduction, and health. Animals not allowed full access to the five-point program may elect to consume available feedstuffs in uneconomical amounts in their attempt to compensate.

The following will serve as a guide when troubleshooting problems associated with the feeding of free-choice minerals, particularly ABC+ Free Choice Minerals.

APPARENT EXCESS CONSUMPTION OF FREE-CHOICE MINERALS

If animals seem to be consuming excess minerals it may seem uneconomical, but in reality it is a symptom of a mineral imbalance. Always check your water, as faulty water is often a major cause of excess mineral consumption.

The following are a few possible causes behind your livestock's excessive free-mineral consumption.

Beef cattle on lush spring pastures
- Lack of available low-protein dry roughage preventing adequate dry matter intake
- High protein and/or nitrate causing stress
- Energy deficiency causing inadequate availability of minerals in grass

Beef cattle on dry summer grass or winter feed
- Low digestibility of feedstuffs due to lack of soluble energy
- Inadequate intake of feedstuffs due to poor digestibility
- Actual mineral deficiencies

Feedlot cattle
- Wet rations causing decreased feed intake
- Excessive amounts of grain with limited roughage causing low ash ration
- Previous mineral deficiencies

Dairy cattle in confinement facilities
- Excessive amounts of grain with limited amounts of roughage resulting in low ash ration
- Wet ration without availability of dry roughage. The cattle can't consume enough feedstuffs and, consequently, enough minerals
- Excessive amounts of protein and/or nitrates
- High production of dairy cows requires more mineral intake than does high production of beef cows

Any situation that tends to limit availability of feed supply may result in uneconomical consumption of free-choice minerals. Uneconomical consumption of free-choice minerals indicates that the animal is attempting to compensate for deficiencies caused by any of the issues listed above.

Uneconomical Consumption of Vitamins A, D, and E (A-Mix from Advanced Biological Concepts)

1. Vitamin A deficiency
- Low carotene content of feedstuffs
- Actual vitamin A deficiency of the animal
- Limited availability of feedstuffs

2. Stress conditions
- Disease
- Calving
- Weaning
- Excess feeding of grain causing low ash ration
- Excess protein of the ration without availability of low-protein roughage for dilution
- Nitrates in the feed and/or water
- Weather stresses, either hot or cold
- Internal and/or external parasites
- High production stress
- Shipping stress
- Lack of available feedstuffs

3. Energy deficiency
- Vitamin A is chemically an alcohol, therefore a contributor of hydrogen energy

Limited Consumption of Free-Choice Minerals

- Low digestibility of feedstuffs
- High protein and/or nitrate ration
- High nitrate content of water
- Lack of available feedstuffs
- Excess ash in the ration
- Ration is adequately balanced
- Mineral feeder located in area not frequented by animals
- Weather doors are closed with new cattle unaccustomed to the feeder
- Minerals in the feeder caked or contaminated
- Aged vitamin A that has oxidized
- Diseased cattle

- High mineral content of water
- Minerals force-fed in the ration
- Deep mudhole in front of feeder
- High carotene content of grass—only half converts to vitamin A, but the other half causes animal to feel that it has adequate vitamin A when it is actually deficient

Cattle Consuming Dirt or Other Foreign Material

- Lack of adequate ash with high grain ration (limited roughage)
- Rumen acidosis caused by excessive amounts of protein and/or nitrates in feedstuffs or water.
- Lack of adequate availability of feedstuffs
- Mineral deficiency of ration that is satisfied by consumption of foreign material
- Diarrhea

MINERAL INTERACTIONS

Lack of dietary boron triggers poor copper metabolism in cattle. Check soil test levels. Try to maintain test levels of boron above 1.0 parts per million.

Do you have iron in your water or in the soil? High iron ties up copper. I see this in my Holsteins some summers when their black coats turn brown and get really rough behind the shoulder blades. During winter when they eat kelp it clears up, but as the grass comes in they stop eating kelp and by midsummer we see the brown hair. We pretty much have only fed kelp as a mineral source for the last ten years. They won't eat regular minerals free choice. We have high-iron soils and lots of iron in the water. This could be because of the excessive iron in the mineral they are eating.

SOME EFFECTS OF EXCESSES AND DEFICIENCIES

It has been known for quite a few years that certain minerals play an important role in animal nutrition. During recent years the list of minerals deemed "necessary to life" has grown steadily. Minerals not only furnish structural material for the growth of bones, teeth, blood, and tissue, but they also are necessary components of many of the enzymes which regulate vital life processes. Not having enough of any one of the "essential" minerals may cause a lack of thrift, poor gains, poor feed conversion, low production of meat or milk, or poor reproduction. Having too much of many of these minerals may result in toxic poisoning, which can impair the health of an animal or even kill it. Not having a balanced ration of many of the minerals may cause symptoms of either excesses or deficiencies or both. Usually these symptoms are noticed only when they are serious enough to cause death or a high veterinary bill, even though the symptoms alone can result in the loss of millions of dollars of profit to farmers, feeders, and ranchers in the livestock industry.

The following list is by no means meant to be a diagnostic guide, but rather a broad outline of some conditions that you may encounter during excesses or deficiencies.

ASH OR FIBER

Dry matter includes everything that is not water. Less than 20 percent dry matter is too wet for proper nutrition. When feedstuff is too wet, the ruminant usually does not obtain adequate nutrition because it is forced to decide between having excess water in the rumen for a time and obtaining sufficient dry matter.

The ash content of the ration should be in a range of 4.85–5.5 percent of dry matter. The ash content of the ration is a measurement of the oxides of the minerals in the ration; however, if minerals have not been added to the rations, the ash content of the ration is a very good measurement of its fiber content. A ration should contain some natural roughage such as hay or dehydrated alfalfa, which is high in ash, and not depend entirely on inorganic minerals.

Effect of an Excess of Ash or Fiber

Excess ash or fiber usually means that a ration is low in energy and should be corrected by increasing feedstuffs low in ash.
1. Ration may be unpalatable
2. Digestibility of the ration is low
3. Butterfat test usually remains high but milk production drops
4. Rate of gain decreases
5. Droppings may be stiff and stack up—constipation
6. Animal cannot eat enough to gain or produce at the maximum rate

Effect of Deficiency of Ash or Fiber

Solubility value of the rations in excess—the ration should be rebalanced to increase feedstuffs high in ash. Feed moves through digestive tract too fast for best absorption and out of the rumen too fast for maximum digestion by bacteria.

1. Poor fill
2. Hard to keep on feed
3. Feed intake varies
4. Butterfat test drops
5. Too much feed going through undigested
6. Rate of gain drops
7. Bloat
8. Loose watery manure

Some Observations on Mineral Consumption

- ADE consumption goes up if there are basic deficiencies in the feeds or the ration, high nitrates or excess protein
- BVC + vitamin C intake increases with stress.
- Calcium consumption may go down in summer and up in winter.
- Iodine consumption increases if nitrates are high or if there is stray voltage or geomagnetic fields.
- Magnesium consumption increases when on spring grass.
- Potassium consumption usually stays level. If it goes up you may want to change rations.
- Sulfur is involved in hair and hoof growth.
- Copper consumption goes up in young stock or with moldy feed. Copper deficiency causes a red tinge to the pigmentation of black hair on affected animals.
- Zinc is associated with feet/hoof health.
- Animals will often drastically alter their mineral consumption within one day of ration changes and will often take more minerals in advance of imminent severe weather changes.

CARBON

Carbon content of the ration should be in a range of 46.09–51 percent of total dry matter. When a ration contains an excess of protein, there has to be a deficiency of carbohydrates. The total amount of protein nitrogen plus primary elements should be 15 percent.

Therefore, 85 percent of an optimum ration must be carbon, hydrogen, and oxygen, which are usually found in the form of carbohydrates, fats, and sugars.

Effect of Excess of Carbon

1. Increases need for hydrogen, oxygen, and nitrogen

Effect of Deficiency of Carbon

1. Decreases need for hydrogen, oxygen, and nitrogen

HYDROGEN

Hydrogen content of the ration should be in a range of 7.83–8.61 percent of total dry matter.

Effect of an Excess of Hydrogen

1. Increased need for nitrogen and oxygen
2. Energy value of the ration is in excess
3. Conditions in rumen too far reduced and bloat is likely
4. Burned rumen (founder or laminitis)

Effect of a Deficiency of Hydrogen

1. Carbon and oxygen are wasted because of fermentation
2. Feed intake is reduced
3. Rate of gain decreases
4. Milk and test drop
5 Amount of undigested feed in droppings increases
6. Starvation
7. Nasal discharge (from clear to colored)
8. Watering eyes
9. Incidence of mucosal disease complex is more prominent
10. Increases need for vitamin A

OXYGEN

Oxygen content of the ratio should be in a range of 41–45 percent of total dry matter

Effect of an Excess of Oxygen

1. Increased need for hydrogen
2. Easily foundered
3. Loose droppings
4. Poor fill
5. Stiffness of gait
6. Depth of body becomes shallow, a "tucked-up or snaky" appearance
7. Amount of undigested grain and roughage in droppings increases
8. Ration is too soluble
9. Milk and butterfat drops
10. Rate of gain decreases or completely stops in severe cases
11. Osmotic pressure in rumen becomes excessive and slows down digestion

Effect of a Deficiency of Oxygen

1. Ration is not soluble
2. Milk production drops but butterfat test usually stays up
3. Rate of gain decreases
4. Digestibility of the ration is low
5. Droppings may be stiff and stack up too high

NITROGEN

Nitrogen content of the ration should be in a range of 2.0–2.3 percent total dry matter.

Effect of an Excess of Nitrogen

1. Increases need for hydrogen
2. Ketosis
3. Scouring
4. Increases incidence of mastitis
5. Milk and test drops
6. Rate of gain decreases
7. More vulnerable to nitrate poisoning

Effect of a Deficiency of Nitrogen

1. Retarded growth
2. Inefficient use of nutrients
3. Reduced appetite
4. Milk production drops
5. Rate of gain decreases
6. Irregular heat periods
7. Reproductive failure

PROTEIN EQUIVALENT (NITROGEN)

Remember: 6.25 x total nitrogen = protein equivalent.

Nitrogen is probably the most important element in ruminant nutrition because it is the major component of proteins, which are a major component of every living cell. A range of 12.5–13.75 percent of dry matter is optimum for all ruminants, as was proven at Panhandle A&M College and the University of Nebraska.

Effect of an Excess of Protein

1. Ketosis
2. Scouring
3. Decreases feed efficiency
4. Requires increase in feedstuff low in protein (corncobs, straw, ear corn, milo)

Effect of a Deficiency of Protein

1. Slowed growth
2. Inefficient use of nutrient (undigested feed in manure)
3. Reduced appetite, wool production, milk production and poor hair coat
4. Irregular heat periods
5. Requires increase in feedstuff high in protein (legume hay, protein supplement)

SULFUR

The optimum amount of sulfur is in a range of .20–.22 percent of the total dry matter. Sulfur is acid in nature. The sulfur-to-nitrogen ratio should be 1:10. Sulfur is necessary for the synthesis of sulfur-bearing amino acids.

Effect of an Excess of Sulfur

1. Creates acid rumen
2. Increases the need for copper
3. Black scours

Effect of a Deficiency of Sulfur

Deficiency of sulfur limits NPN (non-protein-nitrogen) utilization.
1. Shedding wool in sheep
2. Poor hair coat
3. Poor hoof, hair, and horn development
4. Excess saliva
5. Watery eyes

POTASSIUM

The optimum amount of potassium is in a range of 0.93–1.02 percent of total dry matter. Potassium is a strong base. If potassium is excessive, the rumen requires more chlorine to excrete the excess as potassium chloride.

Effect of an Excess of Potassium

Excess potassium is excreted quickly in the urine but this may cause a wash-out situation, which can disturb the calcium-phosphorus balance and result in secondary effects concerning those elements.
1. Alkaline rumen, unless excess chlorine is also present
2. Slows down bacterial growth and multiplication
3. Poor feed efficiency
4. Pressure inside the cell is too great for movement of food into the cell

Effect of a Deficiency of Potassium

1. Decreases carbohydrate utilization.
2. Slows growth
3. Reduced appetite
4. Muscular weakness
5. Nervous disorders
6. Potassium needs to be supplied daily because there is no appreciable reserve

SODIUM

The optimum amount of sodium is in a range of 0.27–0.3 percent of the total dry matter. Generally, 90 percent of all rations are usually short of this element. Sodium is strongly alkaline.

Effect of an Excess of Sodium

1. Swelling due to excess water retention
2. Creates alkaline rumen—may be excessive
3. Slows down bacterial growth
4. Poor utilization of non-protein nitrogen

Effect of a Deficiency of Sodium

1. Decreases utilization of protein and energy
2. Rough hair coat
3. Retarded growth
4. Loss of appetite
5. Poor reproduction
6. Depraved appetite
7. Acidosis

CALCIUM

The optimum amount of calcium is in a range of 0.45–0.53 percent of the total dry matter. Calcium is alkaline.

Effect of an Excess of Calcium

1. Decreases availability of protein, phosphorus, iodine, iron, manganese, zinc, and magnesium
2. Birth paralysis
3. Depresses rate and economy of gain
4. Increased incidence of milk fever
5. Ties up fatty acids in a form which is not usable

Effect of a Deficiency of Calcium

1. Bone growth severely impaired, resulting in lameness
2. Increases need for vitamin D_2
3. Depraved appetite
4. Arched back

5. No vigor

6. Reduced milk production

7. Increased milk fever

MAGNESIUM

The optimum amount of magnesium is in a range of 0.29–0.3 percent of the total dry matter. Magnesium is alkaline.

Effect of an Excess of Magnesium

1. Increases need for phosphorus and other elements

Effect of a Deficiency of Magnesium

1. Irritability

2. Irregular gait or shifting lameness

3. Weak pastern

4. Muscle tremors

5. Grass tetany (animals temporarily blinded, may turn in circles until balance is completely lost, frothing at the mouth)

SILICON

The optimum amount of silicon is in a range of 0.33–0.36 percent of total dry matter. Excess amounts will slow down passage of food through the rumen. Silicon is acid in nature.

Effect of an Excess of Silicon

1. Decreases digestibility and palatability

Effect of a Deficiency of Silicon

1. Slows down growth and multiplication of rumen bacteria

2. Poor fill

3. Depraved appetite

4. Rumenitis

PHOSPHORUS

The optimum amount of phosphorus is in a range of 0.37–0.41 percent of the total dry matter. An excess amount of calcium will increase the need for phosphorus. These elements go hand in hand. There is a definite ratio between calcium and phosphorus. When calcium is excessive, cattle will eat phosphorus to an excess and then excrete both calcium and phosphorus down to optimum. Phosphorus is acidic in nature.

Effect of an Excess of Phosphorus

Excess phosphorus causes an imbalance of zinc, manganese, magnesium, calcium, iron, and other elements, and symptoms of excess phosphorus are the same as deficiencies of the other elements because it ties them up as insoluble phosphate salts, which are unusable by the animal.
1. Increases need for iron, aluminum, calcium, magnesium, zinc, and manganese
2. Poor skeletal growth

Effect of a Deficiency of Phosphorus

Increases need for vitamin D. Deficiency can be created by excess iron, aluminum, calcium, and magnesium.
1. Depraved appetite—chewing wood, bones, dirt, etc.
2. No heat period, delayed heat period, silent heat period, or prolonged interval between calving and first heat period
3. Depressed appetite, reduced rate of gain, milk production falls off
4. Higher incidence of bloat
5. Milk fever in dairy herds

CHLORINE

The optimum amount of chlorine is in a range of 0.42–0.46 percent of the total dry matter. Chlorine is a strong acid.

Effect of an Excess of Chlorine

1. Swelling due to excess water retention in the tissue
2. Creates acid rumen
3. Increases need for iodine
4. Increased incidence of downer cows and grass tetany

Effect of a Deficiency of Chlorine

1. Loss of appetite and weight
2. Poor hair coat
3. Hyperalkalinity—tetany—death

TRACE MINERALS

Trace minerals are reported as parts per million (ppm) on a dry matter basis (1 percent equals 10,000 ppm).

The range of optimum amounts of trace elements measured as parts per million of total dry matter are as follows:

Iron	100–200 ppm
Nickel	0.5–1.0 ppm
Aluminum	60–120 ppm
Selenium	0.1–0.5 ppm
Manganese	60–120 ppm
Chromium	0.5–1.0 ppm
Zinc	60–120 ppm
Fluorine	30–50 ppm
Copper	10–20 ppm
Boron	10–20 ppm
Molybdenum	1–2 ppm
Iodine	0.5–1 ppm
Cobalt	0.5–1 ppm

Effect of an Excess of Iron
1. Interferes with phosphorus adsorption
2. Requires use of sodium or potassium bicarbonate to precipitate iron excess
3. Dark, almost black manure

Effect of a Deficiency of Iron
1. Anemia—most likely to occur in calves because milk is low and little iron passes across fetal membranes
2. Cow and calf operation can show anemia and be more susceptible to diseases
3. Calves born weak or dead

Effect of an Excess of Aluminum
1. Increases need for phosphorus

Effect of a Deficiency of Aluminum

Because of its prevalence, a deficiency of aluminum is not usually a practical problem. Under controlled clinical conditions it has been tied in with conversion of energy.

1. Leg deformities with over-knuckling in calves
2. Egg not formed correctly
3. Degeneration of testicles
4. Offspring born dead
5. Delayed heat periods
6. Shortage created by excess of calcium and phosphorus
7. Sterility

Effect of an Excess of Manganese

1. Interferes with calcium and phosphorus adsorption
2. Interferes with utilization causing iron-deficiency anemia

Effect of a Deficiency of Manganese

1. Leg deformities with over-knuckling, lameness, enlarged joints
2. Deformed young at birth
3. Abortion
4. Delayed estrus
5. Egg not formed correctly
6. Decreased sex drive and sperm formation
7. Decreased carbohydrate utilization

Effect of an Excess of Zinc

1. Interferes with utilization of copper and iron, bringing about anemia

Effect of a Deficiency of Zinc

1. Growth failure
2. Lesions of the skin
3. Legs tender, easily injured, raw, bleeding, and weak
4. Poor hair coat, bald spots
5. Poor feed efficiency
6. Poor reproduction

Effect of an Excess of Boron

1. Diarrhea
2. Increased flow of urine
3. Visual disturbances

Effect of a Deficiency of Boron

1. Reduces rate of growth and rumen bacteria

Effect of an Excess of Copper

1. Degeneration of liver, distended gallbladder, and swollen, black kidneys
2. Blood in urine
3. Poor utilization of nitrogen
4. Yellowish-brown mucous membranes about the eye and mouth

Effect of a Deficiency of Copper

1. Created by excess of molybdenum and cobalt
2. Anemia due to poor iron utilization
3. Depressed growth
4. Depigmentation of hair and abnormal hair growth
5. Impaired reproductive performance, heat failure, abortion
6. Scouring
7. Bones become fragile
8. Retained placenta and difficulty in calving
9. Muscular incoordination in young lambs and stringy wool

Effect of an Excess of Molybdenum

1. Makes copper unavailable
2. Depigmentation of hair
3. Severe scouring
4. Dehydration
5. Arching of back
6. Weakness
7. Brittle bones

Effect of a Deficiency of Molybdenum

1. Created by excess of sulfur
2. Slows down cellulose digestion
3. Calcium deposits in kidneys
4. Chronic copper poisoning—depending on level of copper
5. Slows down the conversion of nitrogen to protein

Holistic Herd
Management

PART 3

13

A Way with Animals

For the scientist who has lived by his faith in the power of reason, the story ends like a bad dream. He has scaled the mountain of ignorance: he is about to conquer the highest peak: as he pulls himself over the final rock, he is greeted by a band of theologians who have been sitting there for centuries.
— Robert Jastrow, *God and the Astronomers*

Everyone in the county seemed to know that Jim had "a way with animals." He was the herdsman for a large purebred beef cattle ranch on the edge of town. His ability to raise calves was legendary.

People started telling me about Jim soon after I began practice in the area. As a young, new graduate from vet school, I didn't expect to be called to such a grand operation anytime soon. But shortly after I opened my office, Jim called me to come out and, as he put it, "help him with a sick calf." It developed that he had already done about everything that could be done but he opined that maybe I could give the calf an IV or something to keep his strength up. To this day I do not know if he called me because he might be able to glean a bit of useful knowledge from a new graduate or because he just wanted to give me a trial run. If it was a test, I must have passed because he continued to call me as the need arose. Over the years, I learned a lot from Jim. He didn't have any secret potions, no magic herbs, no tricks up his sleeve—he just had a way with animals!

Looking back, I am thankful that he gave me a chance to further my own veterinary education by allowing me to watch a real animal "healer" at work. Jim's most important lesson was that there is a lot more to healing than surgery, drugs, antibiotics, IVs, vitamins, herbs, or anything else on the physical plane. He showed me that there is another whole dimension to healing, that of a caring touch that carries with it an inexplicable transfer of healing energy from the healer to the patient. I can't explain it, I don't even have a good name for it, but I know that it exists, for I have seen it at work.

Our modern medical science has not yet advanced far enough to quantify or explain this type of healing. Without "scientific proof" many will scoff, ridicule, and label as quackery anything that they cannot explain. So be it. To anyone who has experienced this phenomenon, no proof is necessary, and to those who have not experienced it, no proof would be acceptable anyway.

MIND/BODY CONCEPT

The first book I read on this subject was *Anatomy of an Illness* by Norman Cousins, in which the author explores the role of humor and a positive mental attitude in his own recovery from a serious disease. Since then there have been many investigations into this mind/body relationship showing that the mind can influence the body in which it resides. If you can accept that, then it's not too great a stretch to accept that it is also possible for a mind to influence a body in which it does not reside.

This knowledge goes back into antiquity. In Biblical times there was the admonition, "Is any sick among you? Let him call for the elders of the church; and let them pray over him, anointing him with oil . . . and the prayer of faith shall raise him up." (James 5: 14–15)

Over twenty centuries ago Aristotle, quoting Perses, declared, "The master's eye doth fat the ox, his foot doth fat the ground." I interpret this to mean that in order to have healthy and productive animals or crops the master must be intimately involved in caring for both.

On a more modern note, Dr. Marvin Cain, a renowned equine acupuncturist, made this short but sage statement: "Thoughts are things." He went on to explain that the positive intent or attitude of the practitioner toward the patient was at the very least an aid to any treatment and at best a powerful healing force in its own right. He also cautioned that a negative intent or attitude could be deleterious to healing.

THE HEALING TRIANGLE, OR THE FALLACY OF DOUBLE-BLIND TESTING

An essential part of modern medical research is the double-blind test to establish a drug's effect. Everything is done to eliminate any bias on the part of the researchers. The results of the test group compared to the control group

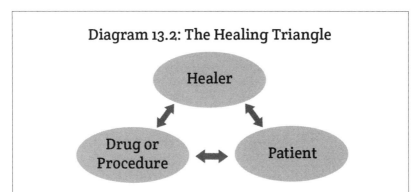

Diagram 13.1: Double-Blind Testing

Drug or Procedure ➡ Patient

Only the effect of the drug or procedure, if any, can be evaluated. Does not take into consideration the probability of patient variability.

Diagram 13.2: The Healing Triangle

Healer

Drug or Procedure ⟷ Patient

In a healing situation, there are interactions between patient and healer, between patient and medication, and probably even between healer and medication.

(which may or may not have received a placebo) give an accurate indication of the drugs usefulness, or so it would seem. In reality, the test only establishes the relationship between the drug and the patient. See diagram 13.1.

A more complete picture of healing is shown in diagram 13.2, which portrays the influence of the practitioner on the patient, on the medication, and ultimately on the entire healing process. If a doctor treats a patient and administers the drug with the same clinical detachment present in the test, he has failed to utilize a most important assist to healing. And if he relies only on tests and sight and never touches the patient, he is missing one of the best modes of communication, diagnosis, and treatment. This explains why some practitioners have great success using a drug or procedure that has been "proven" by double-blind research to have no effect.

It could also explain why folks who believe in the beneficial effects of diatomaceous earth have good results using it as a wormer while those with a negative attitude toward it have negative results. Unfortunately, for some "scientific" types, knowledge often gets in the way of wisdom.

The Healing Triangle also explains why retroactive studies of patients who received a particular drug as part of a treatment program by a caring physician may show a markedly greater success rate than would be indicated by the double-blind study.

SOME OBSERVATIONS

People that have a way with animals tend to employ a more hands-on approach to healing such as chiropractic massage and acupuncture. Acupuncture diagnosis is based in part on noting the response when touching certain points on the body. It is a sort of a Braille reading of the animal's state of health.

I believe that this gift of healing is somewhat species specific. A vet could be fantastic with cattle and lousy with horses, not because of a lack of knowledge but because of a lack of empathy. Most people (vets included) have differing levels of affinity for different species. I know I did; I could do almost anything with horses but would frequently get clawed by my cat patients.

I have heard livestock owners occasionally complain that their vet doesn't like or isn't very good at treating certain species, such as horses, goats, pets, or others. This may be true not because they don't like these particular animals, but because their inexperience with them may make them uncomfortable or even apprehensive when they are called on to treat them. A fearful or suspicious attitude on the part of the owner only increases the vet's feeling of discomfort or inadequacy. For whatever reason, if your vet feels uncomfortable or even mildly fearful treating certain species, his or her results will probably suffer.

Whether a person has a positive or negative attitude toward animals is especially important when hiring that person to care for your animals, such as a vet, a herdsman, a milker, or a trainer. If a person is locked into a position dealing with livestock and is apathetic or has negative feelings toward his job, the animals will sense this, and that person will probably never be a good herdsman or develop any intuitive healing skills.

CAN A HEALING TOUCH BE DEVELOPED?

I believe that almost everyone has an innate healing ability, but not all abilities are at the same level. Some, such as horse whisperers and natural-born healers, have this gift to a very high degree. Others may have this talent at lower but still very effective levels. This ability will probably never surface if you do not believe in it or if you never have occasion to need it. As with many skills, this one is enhanced by use.

Cultivating a Way with Animals

In order to cultivate a way with animals, you must have at least a partial acceptance of the concept that a positive mental attitude can affect the health of your animals, and you must have a positive expectation that you can develop this ability.

You must eliminate all fear of or negative attitudes toward your animals. It is well known that animals can detect fear in humans and will often take advantage of this fear by becoming more aggressive. If you are fearful you will not be able to develop the rapport necessary for a healing touch. You must be at ease around animals and enjoy working with them.

You must watch and study your animals as they relate to members of their own species. To the extent that you can mimic their intraspecies body language, you will help them become more comfortable in your presence and you in theirs.

You must establish a physical bond with your animals by grooming them, touching them, and petting them as often as possible.

Above all else, to have "a way with animals" you must remember that "thoughts are things!"

14

....

Addressing Milk Fever in Your Organic Dairy Herd

"It's all about internal mineral balance!"

One of your best cows calved a couple of days ago and now she's down, lying on her sternum, head lying along her side with a kink in her neck. Her eyes are glazed over, pupils dilated, and she can't get up. If observed earlier she may have been off her feed and exhibiting muscle tremors and an unsteady gait. This is an easy diagnosis for most dairymen to make: milk fever, parturient paresis (calving paralysis), or hypocalcemia (low calcium).

Whatever term you use, if left untreated this condition can result in death in a few hours.

I believe that almost all dairy cows suffer from some degree of low blood calcium at calving time. Most cases are subclinical in nature and do not show the classical signs described above. Calcium is necessary for all muscle function. Even moderately low blood calcium can predispose an animal to calving problems, retained placentas, uterine prolapse, and reduced reproductive performance as well as digestive and metabolic disorders such as displaced abomasum and ketosis. Low blood calcium affects the immune response and may be a factor in mastitis, metritis, and other infections.

Incidence of this condition may vary from 3 percent to as high as 30 percent in some herds. Estimated profit loss from lost production, death, and veterinary costs associated with clinical cases of milk fever range as high as $225 per episode, and the losses from subclinical milk fever may be even higher but are more difficult to measure. Some old-timers say that if a cow "yawns" when you pinch her withers it indicates low blood calcium. Hmmm?

The standard treatment for this emergency is calcium borogluconate. It may be administered intravenously, subcutaneously, or intraperitoneally. If the animal does not respond, a solution containing magnesium and phosphorus along with calcium may be indicated. In early cases or as a preventative in high-risk cows, liquid calcium or calcium chloride gels given orally may be beneficial (always check with your certifier).

Different authorities cite different causes for milk fever. In the past, excess calcium was considered the culprit and limiting calcium levels in the dry cow ration was the standard recommendation. Some blame the high potassium in legumes and some grasses caused by inappropriate fertilizer practices. Low calcium, high calcium, high potassium, low phosphorus, low or high vitamin D, low magnesium, reduced mineral adsorption if rumen

---

Hey, Doc, Waddaya Got for Drying Up a Cow?

Many dairymen approach the dry-cow period with fear and trepidation because so many things can go wrong during this critical time. It is a fact that if anything does go wrong, the effects will probably last for the entire lactation. Conversely, any correction or support given during this period of reprogramming will affect the entire lactation for the better.

Almost everyone is aware of the basic management practices that are the foundation of animal health in general and udder health in particular. In this section, I would like to explore several oft-overlooked principles and procedures that have a strong influence on udder health.

The dry period is divided into three phases. First is a period of involution of the secretory tissue, or the drying-off period, which lasts two to three weeks. Second is a steady state of little metabolic activity. Last is a period of tissue regeneration and colostrum production (two to three weeks).

CARE OF THE NON-LACTATING UDDER

Drying off is a critical time for udder health, and it sets the stage for the next lactation. Any extra care given at this time will pay big dividends throughout the next lactation. Prepare the cow for the stressful transition from lactating to non-lactating by using your favorite herbs, homeopathy preparations, colostrum products, acupuncture, or other practices to boost her immune system and help relieve stress.

If she is a problem cow, culture and treat a couple of weeks prior to dry off. If the cow is producing less than sixty to sixty-five pounds per day after this period of preparation, just quit milking her. She must have a tight udder for about five days for her hormonal system to get the message to quit producing milk. Milking her out to relieve the pressure and discomfort before this time is up only prolongs the process.

After about five days, when the udder swelling begins to recede, sanitize the teats and milk out some milk. Normal-appearing milk indicates a healthy udder. If this is the case, completely milk out the udder, sanitize the teats, and rejoice in the knowledge that, for now at least, the udder is healthy.

Occasionally at this time the milk will show abnormalities such as chunks, clots, wateriness, sliminess, bloody streaks, or anything that does not look like normal milk. In that event, milk out the udder, begin your treatment of choice, and rejoice that you have discovered the problem before it gets worse. Continue the treatment, check the milk, and strip out the udder every few days for as long as necessary to clear up the problem. If you let her go completely dry while she has an infection, she will almost certainly have the same problem when she freshens.

If drying off was accomplished successfully, the next critical time for the udder begins about two weeks before freshening and continues until a week or so afterwards. When the cow begins to "bag-up" and has a tight udder, sanitize her teats, milk out some milk, and examine it. Early in the bagging-up phase, normal secretion will usually resemble a clear, amber fluid, somewhat like honey, and progress from that to regular milk as she gets closer to calving. If normal, be happy.

If the secretion is abnormal—chunky, clotted, stringy, slimy, or bloody—milk her out completely and begin your favorite treatment. Continue to milk her twice a day until she freshens. This prepartum milking procedure will save many udders that would normally be lost if the infection were allowed to go unchecked all the way to calving.

Colostrum is produced shortly before calving. Save the milk right before and after the birth and give it to the calves. It will provide all the protection they need, even though the volume will be less.

These procedures provide a way to check the status of the udder at key periods during the dry period and allow you to begin remedial action if and when a problem occurs. If you follow these procedures you will know 100 percent more about udder health than those who only infuse with antibiotics at dry off and then wait until freshening to see if it worked or not.

pH is over 6.8 to 7.2, water pH over 8.5 have all been implicated at one time or another. I guess you can just take your pick. In truth, all these factors play a part, and the common denominator is a "mineral imbalance." While mineral balance is important to animal health at any time, it is especially critical for the dairy cow at calving time.

During the dry-cow period, and especially in the last three weeks before calving, if the calcium-phosphorus ratio is 1:1, or even higher in calcium, there is a relative deficiency of phosphorus. To compensate for this deficit, the body sets up to reject calcium and to absorb phosphorus. After calving, it takes seventy-two hours for the metabolism to readjust to absorb adequate amounts of calcium.

As the cow approaches calving, large amounts of calcium are drained from the blood reserve to form colostrum (high in calcium) and to begin milk production. At calving, the sudden increased demand for calcium by the mammary gland depletes blood calcium faster than it can be replenished from other body reserves, and thus the stage is set for hypocalcemia.

The key to prevention of milk fever is management of the close-up dry cow.

1. All health begins in the soil. Strive for crops grown on highly mineralized, high-organic-matter soils that are free from residues of insecticides, herbicides and GMO sources.

2. Feed a high-forage, low-grain ration. A cow is a ruminant, don't feed her like a hog. Avoid alfalfa and other feeds or forages that are high in calcium and potassium.

3. Feed an enzyme product with good levels of phytase to release the naturally chelated minerals already present in your feeds. Minerals from this source are much more available than minerals from ground-up rocks added to the ration. This not only benefits the health of your animals but also saves money by the more efficient utilization of homegrown feedstuffs.

4. Allow your animals to adjust their own mineral needs by providing individually and free choice a highly available source of phosphorus (monosodium phosphate) along with sources of calcium, magnesium, potassium, and trace minerals. Dicalcium phosphate is not suitable for this purpose because of its high ratio of calcium to phosphorus. Monosodium phosphate is the most expensive source and not generally used in the feed industry. The quality of ingredients used can vary greatly. Check labels; all minerals are not the same. Organically certified commercial products that meet these criteria are available.

Milk fever is not a disease but only the clinical expression of a mineral imbalance at a period of physiological stress. While the final expression of milk fever is caused by low blood calcium, the predisposing cause is either low phosphorus in the ration or sources of phosphorus that are relatively unavailable. What an animal actually absorbs into its system is the only thing that counts.

It's all about internal mineral balance!

15

······················

A Holistic Response
to Mastitis

"Hey, Doc, waddaya got for mastitis?" is a question posed by dairymen everywhere. I wish I had a good answer. Treatments range from frequently stripping out the udder to the newest antibiotic or immune stimulant. Fortunately, many treatments are successful. But some treatments only suppress the symptoms, and when the effect of the treatment wears off the symptoms return with a vengeance. Unfortunately, any success with treatment often interferes with the need or desire to address the actual cause of the problems. Holistic veterinary medicine may have some insights into this problem, insights that are often overlooked by today's dairymen.

I think holistic practitioners approach problems with a different mindset. They try to look beyond the immediate symptoms and search for, and remove, any predisposing cause or causes. They view the patient not only as an individual but also as a part of the ecosystem in which it lives. Finally, a true holistic practitioner will emphasize holistic animal health management (proactive) in addition to just treating the symptoms (reactive), whether the treatment is holistic or conventional. All dairies have constraints imposed on them by natural principles and the innate nature of the cow. One can either manage according to these principles and enhance animal health and profit or disregard these principles and reap the consequences of impaired herd health. Holistic vet medicine is not about new, high technology or old, low technology but appropriate technology. It is definitely not the

Originally printed in the June 2007 issue of *The Progressive Dairyman*.

conventional system minus the drugs, nor is it just the replacement of a conventional treatment with a natural remedy.

Let me give you an actual example. I recently received a phone call from a veterinarian who has been working with an organic herd that has a mastitis and high SCC problem. Milk cultures consistently revealed strep bacteria. Since this was an organic herd, his treatment options were limited. He had tried various treatments including herbs, tinctures, homeopathy, and colostrum whey products, all to little effect. He had consulted with an "organic" vet at a university and received the standard conventional recommendations: identify the problem animals, milk them last, sell the really bad ones, and treat the rest with whatever their certifier allows. Good advice, but only a Band-Aid. It manages the symptoms but not the cause. As our conversation proceeded, I asked him a couple of questions:

Have you checked for stray voltage?

How long after prepping begins are the units attached?

He had not checked those items but he did his homework and later reported that their electrician did not find any stray voltage. However, he had timed the interval between initial prepping and putting on the units to be somewhat over four minutes—way too long!

All good dairymen know how important it is to properly prep cows. The best stimulus to the "let-down" reflex mimics the suckling of the offspring: warmth, moisture, some pressure or massage, and removing milk. When these or similar stimuli are applied as the cow is being prepared for milking, oxytocin is released. Within about a minute, myoepithelial cells surrounding the alveoli contract, thus forcing milk out into the duct system. If milking is delayed much past one minute, oxytocin begins to clear the system and the oxytocin reflex does not proceed to completion. If one does not "prep" adequately and does not begin milking within one minute, milk yield decreases and residual milk increases. As a general rule, anything that interferes with the initiation or completion of the oxytocin reflex results in excess residual milk in the udder. Residual milk is not milk that could be removed by extra stripping but milk that has not been fully expressed from the alveoli. Residual milk makes great food for bacteria. The more you leave in, the higher the chance for infection.

If culturing reveals streptococcus as the predominant bacteria, there are two main areas that need to be checked: stray voltage and improper milking procedures, especially prep time.

If there is stray voltage present and the cow anticipates getting shocked when she enters the milking area or when the units are attached, she will be stressed and fearful. The resulting release of adrenalin interferes with the initiation of the oxytocin reflex, the animal does not let down her milk, production goes down, and residual milk is increased. If cows are jumpy in the barn or have a high incidence of strep mastitis, it is wise to check for stray voltage. If you can measure it, then take steps to get rid of it. The results will speak for themselves.

If milking procedures are not choreographed to ensure that milking units are attached to the cow and taking away milk within about sixty seconds after the start of prepping, the oxytocin reflex will be impaired, increasing the residual milk and thus opening the door for strep mastitis.

Here's another example. An older couple was milking cows in a double twelve milking parlor that had been built when the kids were helping with the dairy. The kids were now gone, and the dairyman fed and cared for the cows and his wife did the milking. They were plagued with strep mastitis. They had tried a multitude of antibiotics and many natural products without much success. I visited the dairy at milking time and watched the milking routine. With only one person milking, they would load one side of the parlor with twelve cows. Then this wonderfully meticulous lady would thoroughly wash and prep all twelve cows before attaching the unit to the first cow prepped—about twelve minutes later. I was able, after a time, to convince her to adjust her routine so that each cow had a unit attached within about sixty seconds after prep started. In only a few days their strep problem was much abated.

Many factors are involved in managing and treating mastitis. In the above instance the overriding predisposing cause was failure to understand and conform to the basic physiological makeup of the cow. When that misunderstanding was corrected, the problem corrected itself. In addition to the most obvious predisposing factors, we also need to consider anything that puts the animals under stress or depresses the immune system. No treatment will be really effective until the cause of the problem is removed or reduced.

"So, Doc, waddaya got for mastitis?" Oddly enough, if the cause of the problem has been removed, the same natural therapies that did not work before will probably now be effective. Colostrum whey products, acupuncture, tinctures, herbs, and homeopathy are all effective when applied by knowledgeable practitioners in herds reasonably free from stress.

The thoughts expressed here are my opinions based on more than fifty years of experience in veterinary medicine, both as a conventional veterinary practitioner and as a holistic dairy consultant. I know some folks will disagree. That is their privilege. I only try to explore options from a holistic mind-set and then look for confirmation from the real experts—in this case the animals in our charge. If we are attentive in our observations and interpret what we see with a holistic mind-set, we can learn a lot from cows. And always remember: "No problem can be solved until all its causes are understood."

EVALUATION OF UDDER HEALTH

One of the best ways to evaluate udder health is by routinely culturing milk from any animal either showing mastitis or lower-than-normal milk production. Over time, these reports will allow you to arrive at a herd profile of the type of infection present. Results interpreted on a herd basis rather than on an individual basis are of great value in managing the herd for maximum health.

Culture reports will not be meaningful if the samples are contaminated. If the germ that ends up in the tube comes from your hand or from a teat that was not properly cleaned, you could be misled into thinking it was the organism causing your problem. Contaminated samples are worse than no sample at all. Results of culturing must always be correlated with symptoms. If an animal has been treated with antibiotics in the previous ten to fourteen days, the results will usually be negative.

CULTURE INTERPRETATION

Almost any bacteria can cause mastitis under certain circumstances, but most mastitis is caused by staphylococcus, streptococcus, *Escherichia coli*, and *Enterobacter* (*Aerobacter*) *aerogenes*. It is not known why at times these bacteria become virulent, but stress is certainly a factor. If a high percentage of samples reveal the same pathogen, this is presumptive evidence of a cause-and-effect relationship between the pathogen and a specific environmental influence. These relationships are not absolute, but they do provide clues about where to look first for answers. The following guidelines may help you match your problem to its cause.

Staphylococcus

Staphylococcus bacteria have the ability to invade living tissue. Any physical damage, however slight, to body tissues opens the door for a staph infection. Of all the bacteria, staphylococcus seems to have the greatest ability to quickly become resistant to antibiotics. Confirmation of this lies in the high incidence of post-surgical, antibiotic-resistant staph infections in humans. This condition is even known as a hospital staph infection.

In dairy situations, two common causes of injured tissue that may lead to a staph infection are improperly adjusted milking equipment and the use of irritating teat dips. Frostbite, stepped-on teats, and other injuries may also be predisposing factors. Don't overlook the possibility of trauma just because you milk by hand. Hard stripping or milking entirely by stripping with wet hands can also damage the teat lining and open the door for staph infection.

If you have an ongoing problem with staph infection, look for anything that causes injury to the teats or udder.

Streptococcus

Streptococci are not generally invasive but live on the surface of the udder tissue and in residual milk that is always present in varying amounts in the udder. Strep infection is generally seen when good milking techniques are lacking. It can also be associated with stray voltage or any other problem that interferes with milk let-down.

If you have an ongoing problem with strep infection, look first for anything that interferes with let-down, milk-out, or anything that increases residual milk.

Escherichia coli

Escherichia coli—known as the manure bacteria—is found in all feces. Mastitis caused by this type of bacteria is thus usually associated with unsanitary conditions. Some observations seem to indicate a higher incidence of E. coli when the ration contains excess protein, high levels of nitrates in feed or water, or the addition of urea or other non-protein nitrogens (NPNs) to the ration.

If you have an ongoing problem with E. coli infection, look for anything that causes unsanitary conditions and check the water and feed for nitrates or excess protein.

Enterobacter aerogenes

Enterobacter (formerly *Aerobacter*) *aerogenes* is often related to contaminated drinking water, especially if animals have access to unsanitary water tanks, ponds, streams, or puddles in the barnyard.

If you have an ongoing problem with this infection, first check for the possibility of a contaminated water supply.

Some laboratories report E. coli, enterobacter and other Gram-negative bacteria (bacteria that cannot be identified using the Gram staining method) simply as "coliforms." If a culture report lists any of these, I would strongly suggest culturing your water if you have not already done so. If the water is contaminated, remedial action should be taken at once.

Corynebacterium bovis

Corynebacterium mastitis is sometimes seen in herds that have a problem with hock and leg abscesses.

LEARNING TO TREAT THE CAUSE

After spending so much time on bacteria, I should point that it is a mistake to approach mastitis strictly as a bacterial problem. There is no question that bacteria are part of the problem, but I believe their role to be more of an effect rather than the actual cause.

Simplistic medical thought encourages us to treat the bacterial infection—the effect—while holistic principles would have us zero in on the cause, which is usually a stress-induced immunosuppression. With that in mind, here are my thoughts on a few recommended treatments for mastitis.

Although it's commonly prescribed, I question whether anything should ever be infused into the udder, except possibly as a last resort. Even under the most sanitary conditions, the risk of introducing pathogens into the udder far outweighs any anticipated benefit. If one must infuse the udder, use a blunt infusion cannula and only insert it about a quarter of an inch (just past the teat sphincter). Inserting the cannula to the full depth—almost an inch in some cases—is known to cause internal damage to the teat lining. Never use an injection needle.

Also consider this: any foreign substance (honey, egg whites, lactobacillus cultures, other folk remedies, and antibiotics) introduced into the udder will act as an irritant and cause a nonspecific inflammatory response (NSIP) with a concurrent increase in white blood cells. The common result is that the NSIP will sweep away any mild mastitis infections along with the foreign substance that originated the NSIP. I believe it is a mistake to speak of these irritants as "cures" when actually the relief from the symptoms of mastitis is a secondary effect of the body ridding itself of the foreign substance. This is not to say that these therapies are not often effective, but I believe it is helpful to know the actual mode of action and the great risk of causing a more severe infection.

One of the best ways to treat mastitis is to strip out the affected udder as often as you can, even as often as every fifteen to thirty minutes if possible. This has the effect of removing bacteria and their toxins, reducing swelling, and improving blood supply. You can augment this procedure with your favorite alternative immunostimulant such as homeopathy, herbs, acupuncture, refined colostrum antibodies, massage with warming liniments, hot or cold compresses, etc.

Whatever the nature of the treatment used, it will usually be unsuccessful until the adverse predisposing factors are removed. When that is accomplished the incidence of clinical mastitis and the need for treatment diminishes dramatically.

16

Sodium for the Prevention of Grass Tetany, Bloat, and Fetal Loss in Herbivores
Associated with High Potassium and Nitrate, and a Sodium Deficiency

T. W. Swerczek and William C. McCaw

Frosts and freezes to pasture forages in the late Spring provided hints as to the cause of the grass tetany syndrome as well as other syndromes associated with an increase in nitrate and reduced sodium in pasture forages.[1,2]

Climatic changes involving frosts and freezes seemingly damaged pastures in mid-western and eastern states especially when they occurred in late Spring. Herbivores, especially horses and cattle, grazing affected pastures often experienced different syndromes related to increased levels of potassium and nitrate. A correlation existed between the severity of damaged forages due to frosts and freezes and the number of losses in livestock. Our first opportunity to investigate equine fetal losses after late frosts and freezes to pasture forages was in May and June of 1980.[3,4] Equine fetuses were affected with several opportunistic bacterial pathogens, which appeared to be secondary to nitrate toxicity. Fetal tissues and pasture forages revealed high nitrate levels.[5] At the same time we also observed other losses occurring in cattle due to grass tetany.

In late spring of 2001, another episode of late frosts and freezes happened which also affected pasture forages. During this period, we again observed fetal losses but also detected more cases of grass tetany and acute bloat in cattle. These cows were grazing on pastures with abundant clover. The cattle were dying of acute bloat, consistent with rumen tympany. This type of bloat was not the so-called legume frothy bloat, but was related to gastrointestinal

Reprinted from *Beef Magazine*, June 2012.

atony. The pathogenesis of this particular bloat appears similar to the grass tetany syndrome because magnesium and calcium are depleted in the blood due to high nitrate, which disturbs muscular tissues of the gastrointestinal tract. Magnesium and calcium are critical for muscular tissues, and when a deficiency exists, atony of the GI-tract occurs, causing the GI-tract to become more prone to torsions due to atony and gas formation.[6] Local bovine practitioners reported that surfactants, commonly used to prevent legume frothy bloat, seemingly were unsuccessful. We found that cattle did not succumb to acute bloating when adequate loose salt was made available. A similar finding, in New Zealand,[7] was observed in sheep that grazed pastures high in potassium and low in sodium. We noted that horses and cattle had higher incidences of intestinal problems, which were not related to legume frothy bloat but resulted from torsion of the large intestine. Animals grazing pastures with adequate sodium were not affected.[7] In 2001, postmortem examinations revealed intestinal displacements and torsion of the large colon, as well as an increase in potassium and nitrate in body tissues. High nitrate was also found in aborted fetuses in 1980 after late Spring frosts and freezes.[5] Additionally, cattle and horses often manifested laminitis. Furthermore, most herbivores had a dramatic increase in reproductive losses along with a host of secondary opportunistic diseases. Because of these diseases we suspected a forage induced electrolyte and mineral imbalance.[8] The fetal losses and secondary opportunistic diseases were suspected to be due to microbial overgrowth in the gut.[9] More importantly, we observed that farms providing adequate salt for animals were having fewer cases of grass tetany, fewer abortions and less death from acute rumen tympany.

A comprehensive review of literature on grass tetany substantiates our findings that sodium is indeed an important factor in the pathogenesis of grass tetany, and confirms our finding that high levels of potassium and nitrogen in pastures and feedstuffs are likely inducing a sodium deficiency along with a mineral and electrolyte imbalance.

Workers in Holland first noted that intensive managed pastures suppressed sodium in pasture forages that were high in potassium and nitrogen. Cows grazing these pastures showed signs of sodium deficiency.[10] Also, Smith and Aines demonstrated that cattle with severe sodium deficiency exhibited clinical signs consistent with grass tetany.[11] Workers in New Zealand noted that increased potassium in herbage decreased the uptake of sodium in pasture grasses and legumes.[7] After frosts and freezes, potassium increases in pasture forages. Damaged pastures after frosts and freezes decrease the uptake of sodium.[12] It appears that magnesium is not affected by frosts and freezes.

In the 1950s, researchers in Europe reported that when pasture forages were fertilized with high potassium and nitrogen, there was a dramatic incidence of grass tetany.[13] During the same time period, there was great interest in intensive grazing of grass. Consequently, farmers in Europe heavily fertilized the pastures with potassium and nitrogen. In the Spring, these workers observed a remarkable increase of grass tetany.[13] It appeared that when only magnesium was increased in the diet, cattle with grass tetany did not respond. Interestingly, these workers also considered that cattle may be experiencing a sodium deficiency after pastures were fertilized with potassium and nitrogen.

The British workers decided to treat affected cattle herds with adequate salt, and not with mineral mixes, nor any additional magnesium. The results were immediate and outstanding because the cases of grass tetany, for the most part, disappeared. Not surprisingly, the same results observed by the British workers 60 year ago were consistent with our findings in affected cattle herds grazing grass pastures with abundant legumes, or pastures recently fertilized with nitrogen. British workers later confirmed that pasture forages fertilized with high potassium and nitrogen did indeed suppress the uptake of sodium.[14,15]

They also observed an immediate increase in milk production in cattle that were not fed additional magnesium but given adequate sodium. After recording these results, they recommended to dairymen, whose cattle were affected with grass tetany, to first change their fertilizer program before adding additional magnesium to pastures and to the diet. Dairymen were also instructed to feed an adequate amount of salt.

Interestingly, British workers did not see an increase in magnesium in the blood of affected animals that were given adequate salt. A plausible explanation for this is that the high potassium in the diet may have suppressed the absorption of magnesium. This is a logical hypothesis that has been proposed by Martens and Schweigel.[16]

However, an additional factor maybe involved. High nitrate in the diet eliminates excessive magnesium and calcium through the urine and feces and consequently lowers the magnesium and calcium, which becomes unavailable and cannot be absorbed from the gastrointestinal tract as Martens and Schweigel proposed. Obviously, high nitrate anions in the diet induce a deficiency of magnesium, calcium and sodium. Sufficient cations are needed in the diet to counterbalance the excess nitrate anions. When adequate sodium is in the diet, the surplus nitrate is eliminated through the urine and feces as sodium nitrate. However, when sodium is deficient, the bi-valent cations are utilized to eliminate the excess nitrate. Because magnesium is more active it is eliminated first followed by calcium. When there is an adequate amount of sodium in the diet the excess nitrate is eliminated as sodium nitrate. As a result, the magnesium and calcium are preserved and becomes readily available to be absorbed in the blood. This hypothesis is proposed in more detail in a report published at growersmineral.com/grass tetany.[6]

European researchers, in previous reports, advocated that additional magnesium might not be necessary in forages and the diet. These researchers also suggested that prolonged feeding of high magnesium seemingly reduced milk production. With our observations in the 1990s, it appeared that feeding high levels of magnesium over an extended amount of time and also reducing the salt in beef cattle might have caused the wasting syndrome as well as a decrease in milk production. Likewise, researchers in California reported similar findings in dairy cattle fed excessive amounts of magnesium. These workers also witnessed a decline in milk production.[17]

When beef cattle are fed mineral mixes, it is difficult to be assured that all cattle are receiving adequate minerals, including sufficient salt. Often, cattle will refuse to consume these mixes if fed free choice. In some cases, especially related to excessive potassium and nitrate, it may be necessary to force feed the minerals and supply additional salt. Most dairy cattle are fed minerals and salt in complete feed rations. Moreover, it is important that salt, preferably in the loose form, be made available at all times free choice for animals that may desire additional salt.

Clearly, when cattle display signs of nitrate toxicity, from pastures or feedstuffs that are excessive in nitrogen, additional nitrogenous compounds should not be added to mineral mixes that are low in salt, because the low salt entices cattle to eat more nitrogenous compounds. This would be counterproductive. On the other hand, if diets are low in protein or other nitrogenous compounds, less magnesium, calcium and sodium are necessary in the rations. However, if the protein or the nitrogenous compounds are high, then higher concentrations of calcium, magnesium, sodium and other cations, like iodine, are essential to counteract the excessive anions, primarily nitrate, and other anions, like sulfate, in the diet.

To be more assured that grass tetany, as well as other syndromes, do not occur it may be necessary to reduce the dietary potassium and nitrogenous feeds and also provide adequate salt to the ration. These findings suggest that when cattle show signs of grass tetany, milk fever or the downer cow syndrome, they should be treated with magnesium and calcium solutions, and be given sodium in the form of sodium bicarbonate and/or sodium chloride. Previous work has demonstrated that animals with magnesium and calcium deficiency recover when adequate sodium is given.

It is difficult to determine the significance of different levels of nitrate in the blood. When these cations are low in the blood, less nitrate is required to induce toxicity. Conversely, if these cations are high, the same level may be insignificant. Because nitrate will be affected by the cations in the blood, perhaps, when magnesium and sodium are below normal, nitrate toxicity should be considered as the cause.

Analytical nitrate tests are often problematic and often produce conflicting results. James D. Crutchfield, research specialist in the Department of Plant and Soil Sciences, University of Kentucky, has developed a newly available microplate test for nitrate. The results obtained from the microplate test seemingly are more consistent and reliable.[18]

References:

1. Swerczek, T.W. Don't Short Salt. *Beef Magazine,* June, 2003, 14.

2. Martens, H. Outstanding Salt Article. *Beef Magazine*, August 3, 2003.

3. Swerczek, T.W. Early Abortion in Thoroughbred Mares. *AAEP 26th Annual Convention.* 1980; Anaheim, Ca. November 29–December 3.

4. Swerczek, T.W. and Douglas, R.H. Early Fetal Loss and Infectious Placentitis in the Mare. *Third International Symposium on Equine Reproduction.1981;* Sydney, Australia. Jan 24-29.

5. Singer, R.H.: Livestock Disease Diagnostic Laboratory, University of Kentucky, Lexington, Ky., Diagnostic records, and Personal communications. 1980-1981.

6. Swerczek, T.W.: Nitrate Toxicity, Sodium Deficiency and the Grass Tetany Syndrome. Available at; growersmineral.com/grass tetany.

7. Dougherty, C.T., Wells, K.L. and Mitchell, G.E. Sodium in Pasture Species and Grazing Livestock. *Agronomy notes.* 1995;28(5). Cooperative

Extension Service, University of Kentucky, College of Agriculture, Lexington, Ky. 40546.

8. Swerczek, T.W., Dougherty, C.T., Crutchfield, Dorton, A, and Layton, G.E., MRLS: A forage induced electrolyte and mineral imbalance. *K.A.E.P. Emerging Disease Seminar.* March 7, 2002, Lexington, Ky.

9. Swerczek, T.W. Saprotrophic Fungi and Bacteria and Commensal Bacteria that Infect Frost-Damages Pastures may be Contributing to Gut Microbial Overgrowth and Lesions Associated with the Mare Reproductive Loss Syndrome. *J. of Equine Veterinary Science.* 2002;(6) 234-237

10. Paterson, R. and Crichton C.H Grass Staggers in Large Scale Dairying on Grass. *Journal of the British Grassland Society.* 1960;15:100; and Fren, A.M., Physiological aspects of the nutrition of dairy cattle. Fifth study meeting *Europ. Assoc. Anim. Prod.1955*; and Personal communications with Frens, A.M., by Paterson and Crichton, 1957.

11. Smith, S.E. and Aines, P.D. Salt requirements of dairy cows. Cornell Univ. agric. Expt. Sta. 1959; Bull. 938.

12. Blevins, D.G., M. Remley, K. Lukaszewski, D. Davis. 2011. The loss of sodium in freeze-damaged tall fescue forage could be a major contributor to spring grass tetany. 2011; Online. Forage and Grazinglands doi:10.1094/FG-2011-0221-02-RS.

13. Paterson, R. and Crichton C.H Grass Staggers in Large Scale Dairying on Grass. *Journal of the British Grassland Society.* 1960;15:100

14. Butler, E.J. The Mineral Element Content of Spring Pasture in Relation to the Occurrence of Grass Tetany and Hypomagnesaemia in Dairy Cows. *J. Agric Soc.* 1963; 60:329.

15. Burns, K.N. and Allcroft, R. Hypomagnesaemia Tetany in Cattle. I. Incidence, aetiology, diagnosis and treatment. *Br. Vet. J.* 1967; 123:340-347.

16. Martens, H. and Schweigel, M.: Pathophysiology of Grass Tetany and Other Hypomagnesemias. In *Veterinary Clinics of North America: Food Animal Practice.* 2000; 16(2) 339-368.

17. Urdaz, J.H. et. al. Importance of Appropriate Amounts of Magnesium in Rations for Dairy Cows. Vet Med Today, Timely Topics in Nutrition. *JAVMA,* 2003; 222(11)1518-1523.

18. Crutchfield J.D. and Grove J.H. A new cadmium reduction device for the microplate determination of nitrate in water, soil, plant tissue, and physiological fluids. *J AOAC Int.* 2011; 94(6):1896-1905.

17

Acupuncture:
How to Read a Cow

*Acupuncture diagnosis is a type of Braille communication
that enables us to read an animal's state of health.*

In 1985 I had the opportunity to attend a veterinary conference which had
as one of its speakers the late Dr. Ralph Johnson, an experienced equine
acupuncturist. I was so enthralled with his presentation that I visited with
him at length after the meeting. Dr. Johnson is self-educated in acupuncture
and was a member of the group that originally founded the International
Veterinary Acupuncture Society. He later became my mentor as I became
more involved with acupuncture and I spent much time with him observing his approach to acupuncture diagnosis and treatment of fine horses at
several large equine breeding and performance stables.

As part of his "stall-side" procedure, Dr. Johnson preferred to *never* talk
to the owner about the patient until after his preliminary examination. He
said that he did not want his diagnostic judgment clouded by someone else's
observation. He wanted to "listen to the horse" without any preconceived
biases. After his examination of the patient, done by manually palpating or
pressing various acupuncture points and noting the response, he would then
make his diagnosis and tell the owner the abnormalities in gait or performance the subject would likely exhibit in his show or athletic performance.
During the times that I had occasion to observe Dr. Johnson at work, his
diagnosis almost always meshed exactly with the owner's observations.

In our first meeting Dr. Johnson recommended that as a starting point
I should investigate the work of Dr. Oswald Kothbauer, an Austrian veterinarian, acupuncture researcher, and lecturer at the University of Veterinary

Medicine in Vienna. Dr. Kothbauer's interest in acupuncture began in 1956 and since that time he has observed, evaluated, and published the results of over 20,000 cases. As part of his investigations of acupuncture, Dr. Kothbauer would correlate known diseases of internal organs with changes in pain reflexes on the surface of the body. He charted these points on the back and body of the cow and found that they closely matched the centuries-old traditional Chinese acupuncture points.

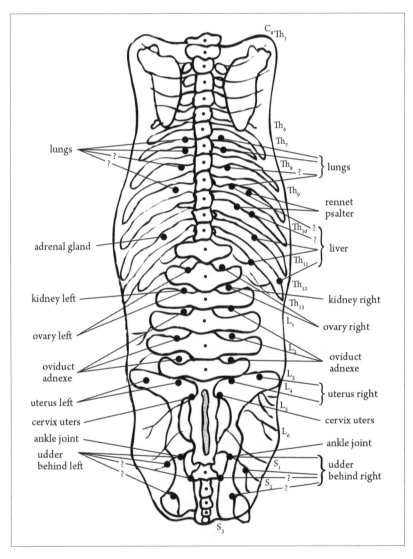

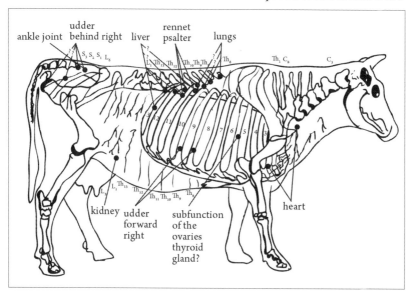

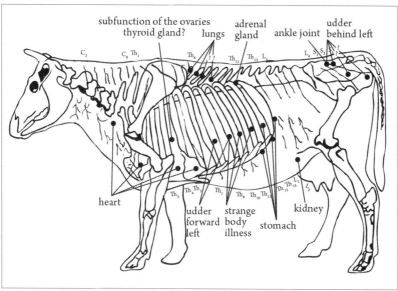

I took these charts to a local dairy where I knew the dairyman would allow me to examine his animals. I asked him to not tell me anything about any cow but to only indicate animals that he knew had identifiable problems. Using Dr. Kothbauer's chart I was able to identify 95 percent of the known problems in the cows I examined, including mastitis, breeding problems, lameness, a case of liver damage (fatty liver syndrome), and one case of metabolic abnormality. I was hooked! The charts worked, and if I could do it so could anyone else.

THE BASIS OF ACUPUNCTURE

A basic premise of acupuncture is that a relationship exists between visceral organs and certain points on the surface of the body. In acupuncture jargon these are called "visceral-cutaneous reflexes." Acupuncture points are classified in various ways. For the purposes of this chapter, we will deal mainly with a few "associated" points and "alarm" points. Tenderness over the associated points (located an inch or so on either side of the spine) indicate a problem with the associated organ/organ function or a problem with the musculoskeletal system over which the meridian travels. Alarm points (located at various sites on the sides, chest, or belly) are stronger indicators of problems with the organ or organ system. In all, there are about 365 named acupuncture points.

A meridian is a map of all points that have a similar relationship. In total there are twelve bilateral paired meridians: lung, large intestine, stomach, spleen, heart, small intestine, bladder, kidney, circulation/sex, triple heater, gallbladder, and liver. Each meridian is named for an organ, an organ system, or the function of an organ system. For example, spleen relates to digestion. Triple heater is generally thought to be associated with endocrine function on three levels: pituitary, adrenal, and gonads. There are two other unpaired centrally located meridians: the governing vessel, which runs on the center line of the back, and the conception vessel, which runs along the center of the ventral surface of the body.

When all the meridians are joined you have a map of the channels through which "chi" (the life force) circulates in a set sequence to nourish the entire body. In Chinese thought, any disruption in the normal flow of chi (excess or deficiency) results in disease. The use of needles or pressure on the points is a way to reestablish the normal flow of chi, resulting in normalization of function, or as some would define it, "a cure." Of course, the application of acupuncture in diagnosis and treatment is much more complex than can be explored here.

Perhaps a simpler way to illustrate the concept is to compare the meridian system to a large, complex electrical circuit with many separate subcircuits, each controlling different lighting appliances or machinery and each protected by fuse boxes or breaker switches. If an energy surge or momentary outage trips a breaker switch, the lights will go out on that particular subcircuit (loss of function or disease has occurred). An examination of the breaker switches will reveal the one that needs to be reset, and when this is done the situation is normalized and the problem has been "cured." In this analogy the breaker switches would roughly compare to the acupuncture points.

The points shown on the charts have been transposed from various sources and adapted to the anatomy of the cow. For the sake of simplicity, these charts only show points that are easily identified and are significant to diagnosis. The points on Chart 1 correspond to some of the traditional "associated" points on the bladder meridian. The points on Charts 2 and 3 roughly correspond to some traditional "alarm" points. Please bear in mind that the location of points is not absolute. The point location varies from species to species and from animal to animal. Indeed, the exact position and actual significance of some acupuncture points are still being debated.

THE DIAGNOSTIC EXAMINATION

The basic examination is performed by pressing each point in turn and noting any pain or tenderness. A pain reflex at any point would indicate a problem of some sort with the corresponding organ or organ system. I would first examine the points on the back and then the sides. Use light pressure at first, and then escalate to moderate or heavy pressure. A response to light pressure usually indicates an acute condition or an excess of chi, while a response only to deeper pressure usually indicates a chronic condition or a chi deficiency. If a point is tender, the most common reaction is for the patient to move away from the pressure. Any reaction, however slight, is significant. Some animals respond to even the slightest touch with a slight twitch of body muscles or just the flick of an ear. On the other extreme, some animals may react violently or aggressively if the points are really painful. The first reaction you note when touching the point is the most meaningful. If you continue pressing on the same point, the response gradually weakens.

Not all animals show a meaningful response to an acupuncture exam. Animals that are "ticklish" or afraid to be touched are not good candidates. Others can be poked and prodded vigorously without showing any response. Extremely debilitated or toxic animals usually do not react.

Acupuncture diagnosis is an excellent tool to use on animals you are considering for purchase. Tenderness on the points may indicate a chronic condition or old lesions from a previous illness. For example, it is not uncommon to have tender "lung" points long after a bout with a respiratory problem. Using these diagnostic techniques on animals before purchase may give you more clues to the actual health status than the seller will tell you, if he even knows about them.

TREATMENT

The best procedure is to regularly perform an acupuncture check on your animals. Point tenderness may precede the symptoms of an actual illness by days or even weeks. This early warning can give you a head start on resolving problems before they surface as a disease condition. Hopefully, the exam will give some indication of the organ or organ system that is affected. There are many ways to use the information thus gained.

The simplest treatment is just to gently massage the sore or tender points. Do this at least daily until the point is no longer sore. Don't forget to investigate and reduce or eliminate the stresses that may be the actual cause of the illness. Once you have identified the problem, you may also want to treat it with other medications or procedures as well as the point massage.

The traditional treatment is to put acupuncture needles into the points. The needles are twirled to stimulate the points. This is usually done for twenty or more minutes every day or two.

Many acupuncturists utilize a procedure called aquapuncture in which they inject the points with a solution of one sort or another. This gives prolonged stimulation to the point and may be repeated in a week if necessary.

Some practitioners use the points only for diagnosis and use other methods to treat the problems thus revealed.

Although these procedures appear simple, there is a learning curve involved when locating the points and interpreting the responses. Don't be discouraged; keep trying. With practice you will probably be able to read a cow as easily as you read this book!

18

Keeping Good Records

My recollections of my uncle Gustav go back to the late 1930s. He raised cattle, hogs, and poultry on a small farm in Gasconade County, Missouri. All his farming was done with horses. He sold his calves and fat hogs to market. During the few months that his cows gave enough milk to make it worthwhile, he and his wife milked them by hand and put the milk through a hand-cranked cream separator. The skim milk was fed to the hogs and the cream was taken to the produce exchange in town and sold, along with any excess eggs. When he got home from his irregular treks to town he always got out his pen, ink, and journal and wrote down all the details of what he had bought and sold that day along with other tidbits of information about prices, weather, current events, and family happenings. His system may seem rudimentary by today's standards, but his records were adequate for his needs.

Today the pen and journal have been replaced by accountants, computer printouts, and check stubs. Sometimes I wonder if it's an improvement or a case of statistical overkill. I recently saw a Dairy Herd Improvement Association (DHIA) report that had almost a thousand pieces of information on the summary sheet alone, plus thirty more entries for each individual cow. Is all this really useful to the average dairyman, or is it provided merely because the information is available in the computer? If one wanted to spend the time and effort, all the required records could still be kept with a pencil and a notebook, but I guess it's quicker and easier to let the computer do the number-crunching. Too much data is intimidating to many folks (me included); maybe that's why so many dairymen subscribe to DHIA and never look at the report!

Regardless of their source, adequate, useful records are the bedrock foundation of any successful business. The primary purpose for keeping production records (other than as bragging power to sell purebreds) is to be able to make management decisions based on reality instead of fantasy. Many good dairymen can quote most of the following essential statistics from memory. Can you?

- **Milk sold per head per day.** This is what you get paid for! Divide milk pick-up by the appropriate number of cow milkings. Add the amount fed to calves and/or poured down the drain because of residue or other problems to get the average daily production.
- **Somatic Cell Count.** A gauge of udder health.
- **Rolling Herd Average.** An average of the previous twelve months production; this measurement tells you where you've been.
- **Projected Rolling Herd Average.** Average daily production times 305 days. It shows you where you're heading.
- **Average "peak" production.**
- **Calving Interval, Days Open,** and **Services per Conception** are measures of reproductive efficiency.
- **Days in Milk**
- **Actual total cost to produce a hundred pounds of milk.**

Even more informative than the actual figures is the trend shown when compared on a regular basis. If your system does not provide you with at least the above records, it may not be adequate for your needs. If you do have good records available and do not use them, then perhaps your own management skills need sharpening.

Finally, here is a rule that should be etched in stone, or perhaps written on the milk-house wall: "The shortest pencil is better than the longest memory." Information is not a record until it is written down. So write it down, now!

19

Treat the Cause, Not the Symptom

Ask any conventional veterinarian how to dry up a dairy cow and prevent new infections and you will usually get a litany of suggestions that really equate to treatment rather than prevention: infuse the udders with antibiotics, inject an immune stimulant and barrier dip the teats, and vaccinate several times with an E. coli product. Unfortunately, you get about the same answers from a lot of holistic or organic vets. Although the recommended products must be certified for use in organic herds, they still fall into the same categories: kill germs in the udder, stimulate an already depressed immune system, cauterize the teat ends with strong chemicals, and vaccinate, vaccinate, vaccinate. These remedies are really akin to only using organic Band-Aids rather than conventional Band-Aids to treat the symptoms.

Here are four items, usually overlooked by organic and conventional vets and dairymen alike, that anyone working with livestock should be aware of when looking to treat the cause, not the symptom.

Mineral imbalances are first and foremost. Almost all domestic animals today suffer from mineral imbalances of one sort or another. This deficit is the direct result of decades of soil depletion and faulty fertilizer practices coupled with confining of animals and limiting or even eliminating any chance they have to balance their nutritional needs by using their own nutritional wisdom. Attempts by nutritionists to remedy this situation by force-feeding minerals in mineral supplements or in total mixed rations usually result in even greater levels of mineral imbalance, and we see cows eating dirt, chewing on wood, and even drinking their own urine.

The second item is water imbalance. Ruminants need three pounds of water for every one pound of dry matter consumed. A complete, meaningful water test should be part of every ration computation. It is not enough to only look at pH and a few major minerals. If imbalances in the water are not properly adjusted for in the final ration, even more massive mineral adsorption and utilization problems may occur.

The third item is nitrogen overload caused by excess nitrates in the feed or water or an imbalance in the carbohydrate/protein ratio. This imbalance could be caused by design as the sale of protein is the profit focus of feed companies. Almost all animal production depends on adequate levels of carbohydrates. Most ration-balancing computer programs are set to meet that need and let values for protein, fat, minerals, etc., float as long as they are adequate. With the feedstuff commonly used this practice often results in excess protein.

Excess protein/nitrogen can also be a problem in grazing herds that graze only short grass. New growth is high in protein, and, without a source of fiber to compensate, the animals are subjected to nitrogen intoxication.

Regardless of the reason for or the method of protein intoxication, the bottom line is that it results in a compromised immune system, which, in turn, results in a myriad of health and production problems.

Fourth and last is vaccine overload. Since most modern medical and veterinary medical thought still acts on the belief that germs cause disease, the misuse of vaccinations in rampant. If vaccines are to work at all, the recipient animal must be in good health. Animals with impaired immune systems from any of the causes listed above will not respond adequately to the vaccine, and indeed the vaccine may weaken the immune system further. Vaccination is a crude Band-Aid at best.

The words *balance* and *imbalance* have been used frequently in this chapter because these concepts are the keys to good health. You cannot attain balance by infusing or injecting stuff out of a bottle, but only by paying attention to at least the four areas listed above.

20

Evaluating Response to Treatment

An ocean storm had caused hundreds of starfish to be stranded on a beach where they would soon perish. A man walking on the beach would stop every few steps, pick up a starfish and fling it back out into the waves. His companion ridiculed his efforts and observed that his puny efforts would make little if any statistical difference to the starfish population as a whole. Undaunted, the man tossed yet another starfish into the sea and replied, "It'll make a big difference to this one!"

I believe this same attitude should apply when treating animals. Even though a negative statistical analysis of one alternative treatment modality may cause some to scoff at and demean all holistic endeavors, the fact remains that most of the time they work, and "It makes a big difference to that one!"

Research statistics aren't really all that useful anyway. Most drug research is akin to insurance company actuary tables, which can project how many houses will burn down in a given time period and area but cannot tell you exactly which houses will be destroyed. In the same way, a drug advertisement may tout a 60 percent effectiveness, but only the individual response to treatment will tell you if your animals are in the 60 percent group or the 40 percent group. In my opinion, the only valid way to evaluate the success of any treatment is to ask: Did it work for you or didn't it?

I did not arrive at this pragmatic outlook in the sterile confines of a library, a laboratory, or a classroom, but in the rough-and-tumble arena of a general farm veterinary practice. Your success as a vet was judged on the basis of results: Did the animals get better or did they not? If you were called to treat an animal and it got better, the owner would probably consult you again should the need arise. If it did not get better, the next time they needed a vet they'd probably call someone else. It didn't help at all to quote figures from the latest drug company research that indicated that the drug *should* have worked at least 60 percent of the time.

Then, as now, a plethora of veterinary drug salesmen called on veterinary clinics to offer the latest fruits of modern veterinary science—a new, more powerful antibiotic; the broader spectrum vaccine; a better insecticide with fewer side effects. Being more gullible in my younger days, I fell for their sales pitch. Occasionally their products would perform as promoted and I would continue to use them. Unfortunately, a lot of the pharmaceuticals and vaccines were not consistently effective, and many caused a variety of side effects guaranteed to make a practitioner look bad. Needless to say, these remedies were seldom used again.

After a few years of less-than-optimum results with conventional medicine, I began to take a closer look at alternative folk medicine as practiced by animal husbandmen for centuries. Some remedies were out and out quackery, but many were based on years of sound empirical observation and made a lot of sense. As I cautiously began to use some of these old folk remedies in my practice, I found that many of them worked as well or better than conventional treatments and were a lot less expensive.

Let me give you an example. A short time after I graduated from vet school, a good friend called me about his mare. Her front legs were so grossly swollen from the knees down that they looked more like tree stumps than legs. Confidently, I opened my medicine bag of modern drugs and began treatment. I used antibiotics; I used antihistamines; I used enzymes; I used steroids, alone and in every combination imaginable. I gave it all I had for over a week and nothing worked; if anything she got worse.

Finally we took her to the university vet clinic. One of my former instructors (one that I had always considered to be old-fashioned and outdated) was assigned to the case. He looked briefly at the mare and gave me a bottle of an old-time remedy, "Dr. X's Leg Brace." His instructions were, "Wet her legs down with this, and cover it with cotton batting and a leg wrap. Do it again in twenty-four hours, if you need to. She'll be okay in a couple of days."

As we were leaving, his good-natured parting shot to me was that I must have missed his class on the day he lectured on this condition.

So, as a last resort, I followed his instructions. By the next morning, only twelve hours later, the swelling had diminished so dramatically that the bandages had peeled off like a loose sock and were lying loose in the stall. I treated her one more time and she made a complete recovery.

What was in the medicine that worked after every modern pharmaceutical had failed? Fluid extract of belladonna, witch hazel, and glycerin in a base of rubbing alcohol.

To this day, I don't know the cause of the swelling, nor can I explain how or why the old remedy worked, but I do know this: "It made a big difference to that one!"

Critics might say, "Why, that stuff couldn't have done anything; she probably recovered on her own," or, "The original drugs finally began to work." To them, any possibility, no matter how farfetched, would be more acceptable than admitting that an old folk remedy had actually worked.

The truth is that conventional medical science today is not far enough advanced to critically evaluate most alternative treatments. Holistic modalities, by their very nature, cannot be analyzed or explained using conventional thinking. Unfortunately, many so-called scientists disparage anything they cannot explain.

The bottom line is, whether animal or human, holistic or conventional, patient response is the only meaningful way to evaluate the efficacy of any treatment.

TREATMENT RESULTS

An old drug response rule-of-thumb states that 25 percent of recipients will show no response, 50 percent will show a beneficial result of one sort or another and the remaining 25 percent will show a greater than normal response (adverse reaction). Obviously, these percentages can vary considerably. Holistic therapy may show a marginally greater incidence of no response but compensate by having almost no side effects. Let's take a closer look at the five possible outcomes of any treatment.

1. **No Response.** It is rare for treatment to have absolutely no effect. I believe there is almost always some effect, even though it may be so slight or subtle that it does not manifest itself by any observable change in the patient's symptoms or condition.

2. **Suppression of Symptoms.** At first, this sudden cessation of symptoms may make the doc or the drug look pretty good. The casual observer may even believe that a cure has taken place. However, in the long term, the patient fails to fully recover and other, more serious symptoms may appear later on. Some vets may consider this new set of symptoms to be a separate condition, but a holistic caregiver recognizes them as an indication that the underlying problem has not been corrected but only covered up. Do not confuse suppression of symptoms with the diminution of symptoms as true recovery takes place.

3. **Palliation or Alleviation** is considered by some to be the most common response to treatment. The severity of the symptoms is reduced or abated, but only as long as treatment is continued. When the treatment "wears off" or is discontinued, the same old symptoms reappear. To maintain relief, it is often necessary to repeat the treatment at more frequent intervals and at higher doses. No cure takes place, and the patient fails to do well overall. This response can be very costly to the owner but lucrative for the practitioner.

4. **A Complete Cure** is the ultimate goal. When this does occur, the results are astonishing. The response is much more than can be explained merely by the removal of symptoms. Health, vitality and productivity are improved even in areas seemingly unrelated to the original condition. Even with this increased vitality, some symptoms may linger for awhile longer. Remember it takes time for a complete recovery to take place. Chronic disease doesn't develop overnight, nor does the body heal itself overnight. When a complete cure does occur, the transformation in the vitality of the patient often exceeds all expectations.

5. **Adverse Reactions or Side Effects.** Adverse drug reactions are common with modern pharmaceuticals and range from mild allergic reactions to anaphylactic shock and sudden death. More and more long-term detrimental effects of these drugs on individuals and the environment are also becoming apparent. According to a recent article in the *Journal of the American Medical Association*, adverse drug reactions are responsible

for 140,000 human fatalities in the United States every year. If livestock owners continue to use modern drugs, I would suggest that they obtain a supply of epinephrine from their vet, along with instructions on how to use it to treat drug reactions.

Adverse side effects from holistic medicines or procedures are uncommon. Those that do occur are mild and nonfatal, unless, of course, they are the result of gross negligence or ignorance.

Keep in mind that occasionally what appear to be adverse side effects may occur as part of the normal healing process. Many times the recovering patient will go through a "healing crisis" before complete recovery takes place. During this "crisis," symptoms may intensify as the body begins to rid itself of toxins as healing progresses. An example of this is often seen when treating mastitis. As the udder begins to heal and the swelling recedes, the formerly dammed-off abnormal milk, pus, and tissue debris are released. The sudden appearance of this "garget" in previously normal-looking milk causes the uninformed to think the mastitis is getting worse when in actuality it is only the body's way of cleansing itself.

CONCLUSION

Practitioners of the healing arts need to be skilled in the use of a variety of therapies and sensitive enough to know which will best serve the needs of each individual patient. When making this choice it is also their responsibility to take into consideration the short-term and long-term effects on the patient, as well as the ultimate effects on the local and global environment.

The real challenge to a good practitioner is to know how to choose the treatment that will be of most benefit to each individual patient. The real challenge to the owner is how to realistically evaluate the response to treatment. For each of them, this is more an art than a science.

Index

About the Authors

Richard J. "Doc" Holliday graduated from the University of Missouri College of Veterinary Medicine in 1959 and has worked in veterinary medicine for over fifty years. Holliday was profoundly affected by reading Louis Bromfield's books *Pleasant Valley* and *Malabar Farms* in high school and credits these works as being his earliest exposure to alternative agriculture and holistic veterinary medicine. Holliday studied the relationship between soil fertility and animal health under the renowned Dr. William Albrecht before conducting his own private mixed veterinary practice in northwest Missouri. During this time Holliday began to work with the concept of feeding self-regulated individual minerals to animals, with great success. Holliday became certified as a veterinary acupuncturist in 1988 and served as the president of the International Veterinary Acupuncture Society from 1992 to 1994. Holliday currently works as the senior veterinary consultant for Helfter Feeds, Inc.

Holliday has been married for sixty years to his childhood sweetheart, Ruth, with whom he has three daughters, fourteen grandchildren, five great-grandsons, and counting. At all times, his goal has been to spread the idea that anyone can prove the fundamental concepts of animal health by watching and learning from animals, who will share their secrets with us if we are attentive.

Jim Helfter, the founder, owner, and CEO of Advanced Biological Concepts, has been dedicated to providing livestock producers with nutritional technology to achieve maximum animal health for the production of drug- and hormone-free meat and milk for over forty years.

Jim's evolution into holistic thought began when he was an aerospace researcher for the Martin Corporation Aerospace Division in Colorado. Jim spent a lot of time studying animals in relation to his research on interplanetary travel and became concerned about the long-term effects of the widespread use of antibiotics in animals. He questioned the wisdom of injecting animals with antibiotics and hormones to treat symptoms or to make livestock grow faster. Jim's experience as an owner and rider of long-distance endurance horses added another dimension to his understanding of nutrition and mineral balance in performance animals as well as food-producing livestock.

Jim's years of hands-on experience taught him that animal health problems are due to nutritional deficiencies from single-source diets and related environmental conditions such as confinement. He has dedicated his company to the prevention of disease through nutrition. The company's mission, "Improve the quality of life for mankind by improving the quality of life for animals through nutrition," is a reflection of Jim's total commitment to this concept.

Under Jim's leadership, Advanced Biological Concepts produces natural and organic supplements and feeds for horses, ruminants (dairy and beef), swine, poultry, fish (aquaponics), and exotics.

Also from Acres U.S.A.

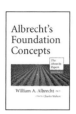

Albrecht's Foundation Concepts
The Albrecht Papers, Vol. I
WILLIAM A. ALBRECHT, PH.D., EDITED BY CHARLES WALTERS
Through Dr. William Albrecht's experiments with growing plants, soils
and their effect on animals, he sustained his theory and observation that
a declining soil fertility, due to a lack of organic material, major elements,
and trace minerals — or a marked imbalance in these nutrients — was
responsible for poor crops and in turn for pathological conditions in animals fed deficient
feeds from soils. These papers addressed to scientists, and especially to farmers who worked
with nature are as valid today as when they were first written. *Softcover, 515 pages.*

Soil Fertility & Animal Health
The Albrecht Papers, Vol. II
WILLIAM A. ALBRECHT, PH.D., EDITED BY CHARLES WALTERS
Albrecht was the premier soil scientist and was dismayed by the rapid
chemicalization of farming that followed WWII. This book is a well-
organized explanation of the relationship between soil fertility and
animal and human health. This is a great book for those new to these
concepts. *Softcover, 192 pages.*

Albrecht on Pastures
The Albrecht Papers, Vol. VI
WILLIAM A. ALBRECHT, PH.D., EDITED BY CHARLES WALTERS
This collection of essays reveals the insights of a brilliant soil scientist
who was ahead of his time in connecting the relationship between soil,
plants and animals. Read about Albrecht's substantiated theory and
observation that insufficient soil fertility was responsible for poor crops,
weeds and thereby a poor diet for the cow in terms of her food choice and her output.
Softcover, 247 pages.

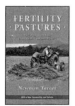

Fertility Pastures
F. NEWMAN TURNER
In *Fertility Pastures*, Turner details his methods of intensive pasture-based
production of beef and dairy cows in a practical guide to profitable, labor-
saving livestock production. He developed a system of complex "herbal
ley mixtures," or blends of pasture grasses and herbs, with each ingredient
chosen to perform an essential function in providing a specific nutrient to
the animal or enhancing the fertility of the soil. He explains his methods of cultivation, seed-
ing and management. He also details the roles individual herbs play in the prevention and
treatment of disease. Featuring a foreword by Joel Salatin. *Softcover, 195 pages.*

The Barn Guide to Treating Dairy Cows Naturally
Practical Organic Cow Care for Farmers
HUBERT J. KARREMAN, V.M.D.

A hands-on barn and field guide designed for quick and easy use, presenting a thorough examination of animals in the barn and then listing symptoms with many pictures of what the farmer is seeing, possible conclusions, and a concise set of treatments. This companion guide to *Treating Dairy Cows Naturally* includes an easy-to-follow visual and hands-on physical exam section, features nearly 100 case studies organized by symptoms, and offers valuable field-tested natural treatments. *Softcover, 191 pages.*

The Keys to Herd Health
JERRY BRUNETTI

A healthy herd begins in such keystone concepts as biodiversity on the farm, acid/alkali balance in feedstuffs, forage quality, and more. In this accessible video, eco-consultant and livestock feed specialist Jerry Brunetti examines these essentials for a successful livestock operation. Brunetti explains the laws of nature in terms farmers can embrace and doles out specific steps you can utilize on your farm right away. Includes a sixteen-page booklet with graphs, tables and data. *DVD format video, 57 minutes.*

Natural Cattle Care
PAT COLEBY

Natural Cattle Care offers a comprehensive analysis of farming techniques that keep the health of the animal in mind. Pat Coleby brings a wealth of animal husbandry experience to bear in this analysis of many serious problems of contemporary farming practices, focusing in particular on how poor soils lead to mineral-deficient plants and ailing farm animals. *Softcover, 198 pages.*

Homeopathy in Organic Livestock Production
GLEN DUPREE, D.V.M.

Written for both organic farmers and homeopaths, Dupree in a logical and comprehensive way, has created a comprehensive and indispensible guide for the application of homeopathy on sustainable livestock farms. Going beyond homeopathic theory and philosophy, *Homeopathy in Organic Livestock Production* contains an extensive discussion of the most common maladies that will help readers recognize symptom complexes and take logical steps to move from patient to remedy, regardless of the species, ailment or the type of farm involved — even if a diagnosis is not known. *Softcover, 176 pages.*

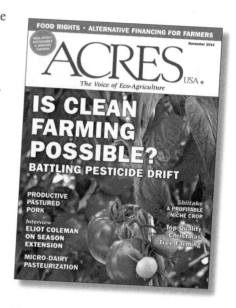